Contents

Preface

The International Reports on the Prevention and Suppression of
Dust in Mining, Tunnelling and Quarrying are published as a result
of the wishes expressed at two meetings of experts held at the
International Labour Office in 1952 and 1955.

The resolutions passed at these meetings were adopted by the
Governing Body of the ILO, and it was recommended that a general
report on all matters pertaining to the prevention and suppression
of dust in mining should be submitted every five years to the Office
by the governments concerned and that these reports should follow a
standard layout to facilitate comparison of the information submitted.

On the basis of the national reports the Office compiles a
general report bringing out aspects in which noteworthy progress has
been made, and the tasks that remain to be accomplished.   The main
purpose of the international reports is thus to provide a synthesis
of the chief information available and to draw the experts' attention to the latest advances in dust control and to the problems
still outstanding in this field.   The four previous reports were
drawn up on these lines.

The various parts of this fifth report have been drawn up
according to a standard layout on the lines set out in the previous
report.   The full texts of the national reports submitted by the
various governments, with their appendices (laws and regulations,
statistics, bibliographical references, technical reports,
recommendations, etc.), are on record at the International Labour
Office and may be obtained on request.

The table below lists, in alphabetical order, the countries
that have contributed to this and the previous reports.

List of countries contributing to
the International Reports on the Prevention and
Suppression of Dust in Mining, Tunnelling and Quarrying

No.		1	2	3	4	5
1	Argentina		x			x
2	Australia	x	x	x	x	x
3	Austria	x	x	x	x	x
4	Belgium	x	x	x		x
5	Brazil					x
6	Burma		x	x	x	x
7	Canada	x	x	x	x	x
8	Cape Verde Islands			x		
9	China		x	x		
10	Cyprus				x	x
11	Czechoslovakia		x	x	x	x
12	Denmark		x			
13	Dominican Republic		x			
14	Ecuador					x
15	Egyptian Arab Republic					x
16	Finland	x		x	x	x
17	France	x	x	x		x
18	Gabon					x
19	German Democratic Republic					x
20	Germany (Federal Republic)	x	x	x	x	x
21	Ghana				x	x
22	Greece		x			x
23	Guatemala					x
24	Guyana				x	
25	Honduras					x
26	India	x	x	x	x	x

Report number

No.		Report number				
		1	2	3	4	5
27	Indonesia			x		x
28	Israel				x	x
29	Italy	x	x	x		
30	Jamaica				x	x
31	Japan	x	x	x		
32	Malagasy Republic			x		x
33	Malaysia					x
34	Malawi					x
35	Mexico					x
36	Morocco			x		x
37	Mozambique			x		
38	Netherlands	x	x	x	x	x
39	New Zealand		x		x	x
40	Niger			x		
41	Nigeria			x		
42	Norway		x		x	x
43	Pakistan				x	x
44	Panama					x
45	Peru					x
46	Philippines			x		x
47	Poland	x	x	x		x
48	Portugal		x	x		
49	Romania					x
50	San Salvador		x			x
51	Senegal					x
52	Singapore				x	x
53	South Africa	x	x	x		
54	Spain			x		x

No.		Report number				
		1	2	3	4	5
55	Sri Lanka	x		x	x	x
56	Sudan				x	x
57	Sweden	x	x	x	x	x
58	Switzerland	x	x	x		x
59	Tanzania				x	
60	Tunisia		x			
61	Turkey		x	x		x
62	Uganda					x
63	United Kingdom	x	x	x	x	x
64	United States	x	x	x	x	x
65	Uruguay		x	x		
66	USSR					x
67	Venezuela					x
68	Yemen PDR					x
69	Zambia				x	x
Totals:	69 countries	18	30	33	25	54

Thus, 54 countries have contributed to the present Fifth International Report. Almost all the reports manifested a growing interest in the problems of dust control in these important industries.

INTRODUCTION

-----

1. MINERALS WORKED

Australia

The report from Australia comprises information obtained from the States of New South Wales, Queensland, Victoria, South Australia, Tasmania and the Northern Territory.

In New South Wales, coal is the principal mineral worked. Seams vary from 3 ft 3 in up to 28 ft (1 to 9 m) in thickness.

In South Australia there is mining of talc, barytes, lead and shales for smelting and quarrying of sandstone and granite.

There are seven underground gold mines and one each of coal, fluorspar, kaolin, antimony and copper in the State of Victoria. Open cast mines include gold, tin, iron ore, coal and brown coal and a large number of quarries are in operation.

In Queensland the minerals worked include coal, copper, lead, zinc, silver, gold, tin, wolfarm, molybdenite, rutile, monazite, ilmenite, bauxite and zircon.   Quarries and clay pits are also worked.

Underground mining in the Northern Territory includes copper and gold with selenium and bismuth as by-products.   There are two iron ore and one manganese open-cast mines as well as a number of stone quarries.

Austria

Dust problems are encountered in the iron mines, the anthracite mines, and also those of graphite, talc, kaolin, felspar and magnesite.   Inspection visits made to tunnelling and drifting operations showed that rock formations were encountered containing up to 36 per cent free silica.

Argentina

The principal minerals worked, in order of importance, are: coal, lead, zinc, iron, sulphur, manganese, wolfram, limestone, gypsum, silver, gold and, to a lesser extent, ores of antimony and boron.   Mining of copper and uranium ores commenced recently. These operations are mostly open-cast mines or quarries.

Belgium

Dust problems are encountered in the coal mines and also in quarries which include those of quartz, sandstone, flint, slate and schists.

Burma

The minerals worked include lead, zinc, silver and coal.

Canada

Information from Canada is subdivided by provinces and makes reference to the following minerals that are worked at present.

In Manitoba, nickel, copper, zinc, tantalum and caesium are recovered.

There is underground mining in New Brunswick of sulphide ores containing lead, zinc, copper and iron.   A further underground operation mines stibnite and there are a number of open-cast coal mines and quarries including limestone and gypsum.

Coal is worked in Nova Scotia.

In Ontario there is mining of quartz gold ores, quartzite and asbestos as well as soapstone, talc and pyrophyllite.

In Saskatchewan the principle underground hard rock mining operations involve uranium ores and copper-zinc ores.   There is also underground mining of potash as well as a number of open-cast mines.

Cyprus

Underground and open-cast mining of iron pyrites, copper pyrites, chromite and asbestos represent the principal pneumoconiosis hazard.   No serious dust problems are encountered in the treatment processes, which are generally wet, with the exception of certain primary crushers where dust suppression measures are utilised.

Czechoslovakia

The pneumoconiosis risk is encountered in the coal mines, which include hard coal, brown coal and lignite, as well as in metal mines which include iron, lead, zinc and copper.   Other operations include the exploitation of limestone, graphite, fluorite, etc.

El Salvador

Minerals extracted include gold and silver.   A special study, covering 709 miners in two mines, was carried out during 1971.

Finland

Of about 40 mining operations in Finland, half include underground workings.   In most of these the percentage of quartz found in the rock is less than 5 per cent, although this figure is higher in certain mines.   One asbestos mine is in operation.

France

    Mines that represent a silicosis risk include the coal mines,
iron mines, other mines particularly those of bauxite, fluorine
minerals and radioactive materials.   There are also a number of
quarries, both underground (slate, baryte) and on surface.   The
principal minerals exploited are coal, the production of which has
dropped to about 32 million tons since the previous five-year
period, and iron ore, of which production remains at about
55 million tons.   Total production of other metalliferous minerals
remains at about 4.5 million tons.   The pneumoconiosis risk is
present in all underground workings as well as in open-cast workings
particularly in certain quarries.   However, it is to be noted that
not only miners, quarrymen, etc. are exposed to this hazard, but
also those working in crushers, screening and sorting plants and in
stone dressing.

Gabon

    The uranium mines of Mounana and Oklo are the most important
mining activities.   They include open-cast and underground workings
producing about 120,000 to 150,000 tons of ore annually, from which
about 400 to 600 tons of enriched uranium are produced.

Germany (F.R.)

    As in previous years, the number of persons exposed to harmful
dust continued to decline due to the closure of a number of mines.

Ghana

    Minerals worked include gold, diamonds. manganese, bauxite and
building materials.   Of these, the principal pneumoconiosis risk
is found in the gold mines which extend down to over 5,000 feet
below surface.

Guatemala

    Minerals worked include ores of antimony, lead and zinc.

India

    Coal and metalliferous mines are both to be found.   Among the
latter are mines of ironstone, limestone, manganese, copper, lead,
zinc, gold, uranium and pyrite.   Not more than one-third of the
coal production is mechanised and in the non-mechanised mines the
dust problem is not considered to be serious.   There are over
2,000 registered metal mines, of which about 400 have underground
workings.   A pneumoconiosis risk is present in these mines.

Indonesia

    A dust problem is encountered in the following operations:
underground gold and coal mining, granite quarrying, tin processing
and smelting, and in open-cast operations during the transport of
minerals such as bauxite, nickel, asphalt and copper.

Israel

Minerals worked include copper, phosphates, marble, limestone, flintclay and construction materials. Potash, bromides and chlorides are extracted from Dead Sea deposits. In the Timna copper mines the ore has been shown to have a free silica content of from 55 to 60 per cent.

Jamaica

In order of economic importance, the minerals worked are: bauxite, gypsum, silica sand and limestone. All mining is open cast and treatment is limited to crushing, drying and alumina extraction.

Malagasy Republic

A dust hazard exists only in granite quarries and in the chromite mines. Other minerals extracted include precious and semi-precious stones and graphite from surface workings and mica from underground operations.

Malaysia

Dust operations are reported in limestone and granite workings.

Morocco

In addition to phosphates, salt and coal, metalliferous minerals extracted include lead, zinc, copper, manganese and ironstone.

Netherlands

The extraction of coal continued to decline during the period under review.

Pakistan

The following minerals are reported as being worked: coal, rock salt, chromite, limestone, gypsum, dolomite, bauxite, silica sand, fireclay and china clay.

Panama

Surface workings for quarrystone and magnetic minerals are the only operations and these do not present a dust hazard.

Philippines

The principal workings are related to the extraction of copper-bearing ore.

Poland

The report gives data only on dust control in chemical mineral mining and in the building materials industry. The chemical minerals considered are potash, sulphur, barium sulphate, anhydrite, gypsum and silica. The deposits worked include underground and open-cast mines together with a mineral-processing station or a crushing and screening plant.

Romania

The following minerals have been worked during the period under review: hard coal, metal ores, non-metallic minerals and construction materials. The rocks contained an average of 10 to 40 per cent free SiO_2. Underground work was predominant.

Senegal

Open-cast workings for phosphate are reported.

Singapore

A pneumoconiosis risk arises in the quarrying of silica-bearing rock. Apart from this, there are no mining or tunnelling operations.

Spain

No minerals are reported whose extraction poses special problems in this field.

Sri Lanka

The only underground mining is for graphite. Felspar, limestone and quartz are won by open-cast or quarrying methods.

Sweden

A full account of the minerals worked appeared in the Second International Report in this series. They include the various iron ores as well as those of manganese and sulphide ores such as those of zinc, copper and lead, etc. Coal mines are also worked and a large number of different kinds of rock are quarried for various purposes.

Switzerland

The report lays stress on the fact that there is practically no mining industry in Switzerland. However, the risk of pneumoconiosis is still important for those who work in tunnels, quarries, foundries and in the ceramics industry.

Turkey

Minerals worked that require preventive or protective measures against harmful dust include cola, lignite, petroleum, copper, zinc, lead, antimony, mercury, bauxite, iron, manganese, chromite, salt, sulphur, natural sodium sulphate, asbestos, magnesite, baryte, natural asphalt and some clays or bentonite.

Uganda

Copper-bearing minerals are worked and these are reported to pose no special dust problem.

United Kingdom

Coal production was reduced from 164.1 million tons to 138.2 million tons during the period under review.   Other minerals were in accordance with the following table:

Mineral	1968 (million tons)	1972 (million tons)
Gravel and sand (incl. silica sand)	103.97	108.64
Limestone	78.17	90.19
Clay shale	36.40	31.48
Chalk, chert and flint	17.63	19.07
Ironstone (incl. gossan)	12.60	8.47
Igneous rock (incl. felspar)	26.18	31.39
Sandstone (incl. silica stone and ganister)	11.52	10.37
China clay, china stone, potters' clay, ball clay and mica clay	3.30	3.52
Fireclay, moulding and pig bed sand	1.44	2.10
Slate	0.07	0.05
Other minerals	0.06	0.62

United Arab Republic

Minerals worked that present a pneumoconiosis risk are phosphates, iron ores, manganese, coal, zinc, lead and talc, as well as building materials.

United States

The mining and mineral industry includes 5,174 coal mines, 599 metal mines, 1,595 non-metal mines and 4,839 stone mines and quarries.   Full statistics on the mineral production have been published and are included in the report from the United States.

Zambia

The principal mineral worked is copper, amounting to about 31.5 million tons of ore during the year 1971.

2. PNEUMOCONIOSIS STATISTICS

As in the case of the previous report on the prevention and suppression of dust in mining, tunnelling and quarrying, the statistics received from the member States varied widely both in detail and in extent. The same procedure has thus been followed of presenting this information in the form in which it was received. It will be seen that they are compiled in various fashions and according to different criteria. No attempt has been made to alter their original presentation in order to render them more comparable.

Argentina

Statistics have not been collected on a uniform basis up to the present time but recent legislation contains provisions for the introduction of an over-all system during the three-year period 1974-77. The total number of persons employed in the mining industry stands at about 28,000 but this figure includes administrative and other personnel.

Australia

New South Wales

No pneumoconiosis statistics for coal mining are at present available comparable to those submitted in the previous report. An up-to-date prevalence study using the ILO/UC classification is currently proceeding.

(a) Numbers of persons exposed to risk (New South Wales coal industry):

Table 1

| Year | Coal face workers | Elsewhere underground | Surface workers(a) | | Total coal industry |
			Underground mines	Open Cuts	
30.6.1968	3 075	5 325	4 078	288	12 766
30.6.1969	3 142	5 568	4 175	329	13 214
30.6.1970	3 410	5 669	4 353	377	13 809
30.6.1971	3 534	5 979	4 473	393	14 379
30.6.1972	3 547	5 714	4 190	463	13 914

(a) Includes administrative and clerical workers.

New South Wales (cont.)

(b) Total periodic routine examinations:

Table 2

Year	Numbers examined
30.6.1968	3 728
30.6.1969	3 828
30.6.1970	3 398
30.6.1971	3 502
30.6.1972	4 434

(c) Numbers of new cases: (as certified for workers' compensation)

N.B. Aged 60 or over are retired miners.
Under 60, mostly still at work and approaching
retirement.

Table 3

Year ending	Incapacity	Under 60	60 and over
30.6.1968	Partial	4	5
	Total	1	0
30.6.1969	Partial	5	7
	Total	0	0
30.6.1970	Partial	3	4
	Total	0	1
30.6.1971	Partial	1	2
	Total	0	0
30.6.1972	Partial	1	1
	Total	0	1

N.B. Degree of incapacity is certified on total assessed lung
incapacity including that due to emphysema, chronic
bronchitis, chronic asthma.

Queensland

A Chest Board determines applications for compensation for
pneumoconiosis and silicosis.

Statistics are not available for:

- total number of pneumoconiotics; and
- deaths from pneumoconiosis.

Queensland (cont.)

The results in the following tables indicate a relatively low incidence of both silicosis and pneumoconiosis. A number of men certified as pneumoconiotics are older than 65 years.

Table 4

For period 1968-1972

Class of mine	Average number of men exposed to risk	Number of new cases of silicosis certified	Number of new cases of pneumoconiosis certified	Number of new cases of anthrosilicosis certified
Metal	3 903	29	-	3
Coal	1 387	-	9	-

Table 5

Pneumoconiosis X-ray readings
For period 1968-1972

Category	Pneumoconiosis	Silicosis	Anthracosilicosis
L	-	-	-
1	2	1	-
2	3	6	1
3	4	22	2
Progressive massive filbrosis	1	5	-

South Australia

There is an onus placed on employees to seek registration with within 21 days of commencing employment in the workings listed in the foregoing section of this report. Physical examination (including chest X-ray) will be arranged by the Board of the Workmen's Compensation (Silicosis) Scheme for any workman whose examination is required under the provisions of this scheme.

Employees are responsible for applying for re-examination should their private medical adviser consider them affected by silicosis.

The employer must supply the Board with a list of all workmen employed by him at six-monthly intervals.

South Australia (cont.)

Table 6

Year	(a) Persons exposed to risk	(b) Total silicotics	(c) New cases	(d) Deaths from silicosis	Persons (e) engaged			
					Sand and shot blasting	Quarrying and treatment	Bituminous hot mix	Silica grinding
1962-63	283	*NA	*NA	*NA	28	248	5	2
1963-64	320	"	"	"	24	289	5	2
1964-65	351	"	"	"	30	314	5	2
1965-66	342	"	"	"	26	308	6	2
1966-67	336	"	"	"	26	303	4	3
1967-68	346	"	"	"	40	298	5	*NA
1968-69	296	"	"	"	33	258	5	"
1969-70	301	"	"	"	33	262	5	"
1970-71	268	"	"	"	22	239	6	"
1971-72	254	"	"	"	18	229	6	"
1972-73	314	"	"	"	17	290	6	"
1973-74	301	"	"	"	17	277	6	"

*NA = not available.

Tasmania

Statistics are compiled by the Workers' (Occupational Diseases) Relief Fund Board from biennial examinations. No figures are available.

Northern Territory

The Health Department holds routine chest X-rays every year for mineworkers in the Northern Territory. No figures are available.

Victoria

Table 7

40 cases of pneumoconiosis notified to
the Industrial Hygiene Division, 1968-1972

Occupation	1968	1969	1970	1971	1972
Coal mining	-	3	2	1	-
Metal mining	9	14	5	4	-
Tunnelling	2	-	-	-	-
Quarrying	-	-	-	-	-
Total	11	17	7	5	-

Austria

Table 1 shows the number of suspected cases of silicosis,
silicosis or silicatosis, the number of recognised cases, and the
number of deaths from this cause.

Table 1

Year	Retained for further examination	New awards	Deaths
1968	61	3	9
1969	41	1	10
1970	45	2	15
1971	47	1	11
1972	40	3	13

It should be noted that comparison of these figures is subject
to reservations because the number of suspected cases indicated in
the first column depends on the results of mass X-ray examinations
carried out.   Each year these examinations cover different branches
of mining with different personnel totals.   Further, the number of
confirmed cases is only a fraction of those reported ill.   In the
case of the deaths, a large proportion of the victims were exposed
to dust in the past before effective measures against dust existed.

Table 2 illustrates the scope of medical supervision of workers
by mass X-ray examinations.

Table 2

Statistics of mass X-ray examinations

Year	Number of undertakings covered	Number of persons examined	Retained for specialist examination	Already under medical supervision
A. Total all mining				
1968	20	808	5	6
1969	7	1 468	10	13
1970	16	787	8	14
1971	16	2 977	24	35
1972	12	565	3	4
B. Coal mining				
1968	1	10	-	-
1969	1	4	-	1
1970	-	-	-	-
1971	1	1 034	17	22
1972	-	-	-	-

Austria (cont.)

Table 2 (cont.)

Statistics of mass X-ray examinations

Year	Number of under- takings covered	Number of persons examined	Retained for specialist examination	Already under medical supervision
C. Metal mining				
1968	2	34	-	-
1969	3	1 426	9	12
1970	1	17	-	-
1971	4	1 408	3	9
1972	1	21	-	-
D. Other mining				
1968	17	764	5	6
1969	3	38	1	-
1970	15	770	8	14
1971	11	535	4	4
1972	11	544	3	4

Burma

Statistics are collected by the mine hospitals established by the Ministry of Health. They show that 3,421 persons were exposed to risk and that no new cases nor deaths from pneumoconiosis were recorded.

Canada

Statistical information from Canada is presented by provinces.

British Columbia

Table 3 presents pneumoconiosis statistics for the Province of British Columbia for the years 1969 to 1973. The Workmen's Compensation Board keep the work history and medical history of all workmen examined for a certificate of fitness and dust exposure occupations. It should be noted that the number of medical examinations does not represent the number of men employed in dust exposure occupations as there are some men leaving the industry each year and new men starting. There are no statistics available on the place of employment, the type of work and duration of exposure.

British Columbia (cont.)

Table 3

Pneumoconiosis statistics for British Columbia

	1969	1970	1971	1972	1973
Number of chest X-rays and medical examinations	5 094	5 190	3 860	4 471	5 908
New pensions granted to workmen with silicosis	14	8	7	14	11
Number of pensioners who have died					
- from silicosis	14	8	9	8	5
- from other causes	9	5	12	10	11
Total number of pensions being paid	314	309	295	291	286

Manitoba

The following figures are given for the year 1973:

(a) Number of persons exposed to risk   5,795
(b) Total number of pneumoconiotics   12 (incl. one asbestosis)
(c) New cases of pneumoconiosis   5 (initial silicosis - new cases)
(d) Death from pneumoconiosis   0 (one death in 1972)
(e) Place of employment - mines and foundries

Pulmonary dysfunction is found to be of higher incidence and occurring at a younger age among Manitoba's foundrymen than in the miners.   These findings are based on mandatory annual medical examinations conducted by the Sanatorium Board and sponsored jointly by the Manitoba Workers Compensation Board and the Department of Health and Social Development.

Licenses are issued to these men by the office of the Occupational Medical Director.

Nova Scotia

The figures quoted are those for the coal mines only (DEVCO) for the period 1968-72.

Table 4

Pneumoconiosis statistics (DEVCO) Nova Scotia

Year	Number of cases	Number of employees exposed
1968	21	4 858
1969	47	3 567
1970	239	3 338
1971	653	3 014
1972	355	2 640

There were 19 deaths due to silicosis reported during the period 1968 to 1974.

Ontario

Table 5

Silicosis in Ontario mines

New silicosis cases found each year - 1968 to 1972
by years of first exposure to dust

Year first expos.	Year found						Total
	Before 1967	1968	1969	1970	1971	1972	
Before 1900	58	-	-	-	-	-	58
1900	5	-	-	-	-	-	5
01	11	-	-	-	-	-	11
02	7	-	-	-	-	-	7
03	17	-	-	-	-	-	17
04	24	-	-	-	-	-	24
1905	22	-	-	-	-	-	22
06	38	-	-	-	-	-	38
07	51	-	-	-	-	-	51
08	34	-	-	-	-	-	34
09	40	-	-	-	-	-	40
1910	63	1	-	-	-	-	64
11	50	1	-	-	-	-	51
12	59	-	-	-	-	-	59
13	103	-	-	-	-	1	104
14	65	-	-	-	-	-	65

Ontario (cont.)

Table 5 (cont.)

Silicosis in Ontario mines

Year first expos.	Year found						Total
	Before 1967	1968	1969	1970	1971	1972	
1915	59	-	-	-	-	-	59
16	59	.-	-	-	-	-	59
17	53	-	-	-	-	-	53
18	43	-	-	-	-	-	43
19	61	1	-	-	-	-	62
1920	59	-	-	-	-	-	59
21	54	-	1	-	-	-	55
22	57	-	-	-	-	-	57
23	88	-	1	-	-	-	89
24	70	-	-	1	-	-	71
1925	40	2	4	-	-	-	46
26	54	2	3	1	1	-	61
27	52	1	1	1	-	-	21
28	45	1	-	2	2	-	50
29	32	4	2	2	-	-	40
1930	18	1	1	1	-	-	21
31	12	-	-	2	-	-	14
32	.4	-	-	-	-	-	4
33	7	-	-	-	-	1	8
34	8	-	1	1	-	1	11
1935	7	-	1	1	3	-	12
36	9	-	-	-	1	1	11
37	1	2	-	-	-	-	3
38	5	-	-	-	1	-	6
39	0	1	-	1	1	-	3
1940	1	2	1	1	-	-	5
41	1	2	1	2	-	1	7
42	4	-	1	-	-	-	5
43	0	-	-	-	-	-	0
44	0	-	-	-	-	-	0
1945	2	-	1	-	1	-	4
46	2	1	3	-	-	-	6
47	5	-	1	-	1	1	8
48	1	-	-	-	-	-	1
49	2	-	-	-	1	-	3
1950	2	1	1	-	-	-	4
51	1	1	1	1	2	-	6
52	2	-	-	2	1	-	5
53	0	-	-	-	-	-	0
54	2	1	-	-	-	1	4
1955	2	2	-	1	-	-	5
56	2	1	-	2	1	1	7
57	1	1	3	1	-	1	7
58	2	2	1	1	3	3	12
59	0	-	-	1	-	1	2

Ontario (cont.)

Table 5 (cont.)

Silicosis in Ontario mines

Year first expos.	Year found						Total
	Before 1967	1968	1969	1970	1971	1972	
1960	1	-	-	-	-	-	1
61	0	-	-	-	-	-	0
62	0	-	-	-	-	1	1
63	0	-	-	-	-	-	0
64	0	-	-	-	-	-	0
1965	0	-	-	-	-	-	0
66	0	-	-	-	-	-	0
67	0	-	-	-	-	-	0
68	0	-	-	-	-	-	0
69	0	-	-	-	-	-	0
1970	0	-	-	-	-	-	0
71	0	-	-	-	-	-	0
73	0	-	-	-	-	-	0
Total	1 577	31	29	25	19	14	1 695

An additional report was received entitled "Causes of death in Ontario uranium miners".   Statistics under this heading have not been included in the present section.   The full report is available.

Cyprus

Table 6 shows the results of initial and periodical examinations of persons employed in dusty occupations for the period under consideration.

Table 6

Pneumoconiosis statistics - Cyprus

Year	No. of persons examined	No. of persons suffering from pneumo.	Deaths from pneumo.	Degree of incapacity				
				0.30%	31-40%	40-60%	60-80%	80-100%
1968	1 105	117	5	37	33	19	11	17
1969	1 334	109	3	31	31	20	7	20
1970	1 262	107	4	24	31	18	14	20
1971	1 180	107	2	15	38	19	9	26
1972	1 065	105	2	10	31	25	10	29

Czechoslovakia

Statistics of pneumoconiosis are not collected on a centralised basis in Czechoslovakia, but detailed records are, however, kept by the occupational health services for each branch of industrial activity.   Thus, for metalliferous and magnesite mines, the number of persons at risk for the years 1968-1972 inclusive have been: 5,403, 5,621, 5,851, 6,120 and 6,320 respectively.

Newly reported cases and deaths from pneumoconiosis are set out in table 7.

Table 7

New cases and deaths from pneumoconiosis - Czechoslovakia

Year	New cases of sili- cosis	Deaths from sili- cosis	New cases of sili- cotuber- culosis	Deaths from sili- cotuber- culosis	New cases of asbes- tosis	Deaths from other forms of pneum.	Total new cases	Total deaths
1968	837	118	114	94	4	24	955	236
1969	755	192	152	107	4	19	911	318
1970	746	195	126	114	4	14	976	323
1971	721	-	142	-	4	-	867	-
1972	575	-	138	-	-	-	713	-

The majority of new cases and deaths were revealed among the age group 60-74.

In relation to the average length of exposure leading to the appearance of silicosis, reports from different branches of industry show the following variations:

- the ceramic industry: 15 to 30 years
- metalliferous mines: 5 to 20 years
- heavy engineering and metallurgical industries:
      20 to 30 years
- civil engineering (tunnelling and other work underground):
      10 to 20 years.

Table 8 relates new cases of pneumoconiosis to the place of employment, occupation and average length of exposure.

Czechoslovakia (cont.)

Table 8

New cases of pneumoconiosis according to place
of work, occupation and average length of exposure
Czechoslovakia

Year	1968	1969	1970	1971	1972
Workplace					
at the face	60	64	61	62	65
drifts, headings	35	31	37	30	31
ancillary services	4	5	1	8	3
others	1	-	1	-	-
Occupation					
rock breakers	70	60	63	54	59
assistant rock					
breakers	25	35	32	40	36
timbermen	3	2	4	4	5
trammers	2	3	1	2	-
Average length of exposure					
less than 15 years	15	14	12	12	11
15 to 20 years	30	26	32	33	34
more than 20 years	55	60	56	55	55

Table 9 shows the number of persons at risk and the number of
new cases of silicosis in quarries and sand treatment plants.

Table 9

Persons at risk and new cases of silicosis
in quarries and sand treatment plants
Czechoslovakia

Year	Number of persons at risk	New cases of silicosis
1968	670	2
1969	581	2
1970	641	1
1971	662	6
1972	652	2

El Salvador

    A study carried out in 1971 on the prevalence of silicosis in
two mines - San Sebastian and San Cristobal - revealed the following
figures (table 10).

Table 10

Positive cases of silicosis
in two mines - El Salvador

	Total		San Sebastian		San Cristobal	
	Number of persons	Per cent	Number of persons	Per cent	Number of persons	Per cent
Positive	75	10.5	23	9.5	52	11.0
Negative	634	89.5	218	90.5	416	89.0
Total	709	100.0	241	100.0	468	1u0.0

    Table 11 indicates the number of years of work in dusty
occupations for workers in the same two mines together with the
number of positive silicosis cases identified and the corresponding
percentage figures.

Table 11

Years of exposure and silicosis cases -
El Salvador

Years worked	Persons examined	Positive cases	Per cent
0-3	211	7	3.3
·4-6	114	5	4.4
7-9	109	11	10.0
10-14	135	21	15.5
over 15	112	30	26.7
unknown	28	1	3.5
Total	709	75	10.5

Finland

Tables 12 and 13 show the number of persons at risk on surface and underground and the total number of cases of pneumoconiosis in all industries verified by the Institute of Occupational Health and reported by insurance companies.

Table 12

Persons at risk and new cases of
pneumoconiosis - Finland

	1968	1969	1970	1971	1972
Total number of workers employed in the mining industry	4 186	5 541	5 490	5 544	5 089
- of them men	3 790	4 826	4 805	4 805	4 409
- of them women	396	715	685	686	680
- of them were employed underground (men)	figure not known	1 565	1 593	1 499	1 523
New cases of silicosis in the mining industry	4	6	8	5	5
Deaths from pneumoconiosis	Exact data on mines only are not available because information on cases is communicated to insurance companies by the undertakings concerned.				

Table 13

Pneumoconiosis cases reported by
insurance companies - Finland

	1968	1969	1970	1971	1972
Quartz dust	19	14	20	18	21
Asbestos dust	13	12	9	9	42
Talc dust	-	1	-	1	-

France

Pneumoconiosis statistics are prepared by the <u>Direction de la Technologie de l'Environnement Industriel et des Mines au Ministère de l'Industrie et de la Recherche as well as by the Caisse Autonome Nationale de Sécurité Sociale dans les Mines</u>.

The former relate to silicotics and other pneumoconiotics at work and are prepared by the companies themselves and transmitted through the chief mining engineers to the central administration.

The latter relate to all silicotics whether at work or not who are in receipt of an invalidity payment.

In the statistics that follow, the words "Mines scheme" and "General scheme" refer to the social security system under which the persons concerned are registered.

It is not possible to determine exactly the number of persons employed underground and on surface as engineers and certain other administrative personnel are excluded from the figures quoted.

For underground quarries, those of baryte and slate represent a silicosis risk.   In the case of surface quarries, the most dangerous are those of granite, gneiss, sandstone, quartzite and silica sand and the most exposed workers are those working in the crushers, screens, sorting and stonecutting and polishing workshops. The statistics refer to about 6,000 to 7,000 persons for whom the degree of exposure varies greatly.

Table 14

Personnel on the books on 31 December of
each year 1968 to 1972 - France

	1968	1969	1970	1971	1972
Coal mines -					
Underground	87 990	78 555	70 727	64 895	57 228
Surface	49 134	45 512	41 861	41 414	39 368
Total	137 124	124 067	112 588	106 309	96 596
Iron mines -					
Underground	8 865	8 336	8 140	7 819	7 297
Surface	3 457	3 233	3 169	2 986	2 737
Total	12 322	11 569	11 309	10 805	10 034
Other -					
Underground	2 869	2 840	2 901	2 830	2 545
Surface	2 313	2 219	2 175	2 087	1 751
Total	5 182	5 059	5 076	4 917	4 296
Slate pits -					
Underground	1 061	1 016	943	747	720
Surface	2 084	2 039	1 872	1 699	1 603
Total	3 145	3 055	2 815	2 446	2 323

France (cont.)

Table 14 (cont.)

	1968	1969	1970	1971	1972
All undertakings in the "Mines scheme" -					
Underground	100 785	90 747	82 711	76 291	67 790
Surface	56 988	53 003	49 077	48 186	45 459
Total	157 773	143 750	131 788	124 477	113 249
Quarries in the "General scheme" -					
Underground	90	94	98	104	100
Surface	5 890	6 256	6 057	6 960	6 900
Total	5 980	6 350	6 155	7 064	7 000

Table 15 shows the total number of silicotics at work in the different mining undertakings.

Table 15

Number of silicotics at work - France

	1968	1969	1970	1971	1972
Coal	21 052	19 420	17 222	15 718	13 541
Iron	132	144	143	151	152
Other mines	63	56	51	54	50
Slate pits	81	78	76	68	75
Total "Mines scheme"	21 328	19 698	17 492	15 991	13 818
"General scheme"	62	63	65	59	60

Table 16 shows the total number of silicotics under the "Mines scheme" at work in mining undertakings or having left their employment, at 31 December of each year.

France (cont.)

Table 16

Total silicotics under the "Mines scheme" - France

	1968	1969	1970	1971	1972
At work	21 328	19 698	17 492	15 991	13 818
Not working	29 236	30 093	32 179	33 143	34 983
Total	50 564	49 791	49 671	49 134	48 801

Table 17 gives the percentage distribution of silicotics at 31 December of each year according to the degree of permanent incapacity which has been recognised. Those shown with 0 per cent have been recognised but do not, or do not yet, receive compensatory payment.

Table 17

Percentage distribution of silicotics according to their recognised permanent incapacity - France

Year	0%	1 to 9%	10 to 19%	20 to 29%	30 to 39%	40 to 49%	50 to 99%	100%	100% with additional indemnity
1. Silicotics at work									
1968	14.9	40.4	28.8	10.2	3.7	1.2	0.8	0.005	-
1969	13.6	40.3	30.0	10.2	4.0	1.2	0.7	0.01	-
1970	12.6	40.7	30.8	10.0	4.0	1.2	0.6	0.01	-
1971	12.0	40.2	31.5	10.3	4.1	1.3	0.6	"	-
1972	11.8	40.6	31.7	10.2	3.8	1.2	0.7	"	-
2. Silicotics not at work									
1968	-	2.3	24.2	15.3	15.1	9.7	25.4	7.2	0.7
1969	-	2.6	24.1	15.1	15.2	9.8	25.6	6.8	0.7
1970	-	4.2	24.4	15.0	15.0	9.3	24.9	6.5	0.7
1971	-	4.6	24.5	14.9	14.8	9.5	24.8	6.3	0.7
1972	-	5.5	25.2	14.8	14.4	9.6	24.0	5.8	0.7
3. Total silicotics									
1968	6.3	18.3	26.3	13.1	10.3	6.1	15.0	4.2	0.4
1969	5.4	17.5	26.4	13.2	10.8	6.4	15.8	4.1	0.4
1970	4.4	17.1	26.7	13.2	11.1	6.5	16.4	4.2	0.4
1971	3.9	16.2	26.8	13.4	11.3	6.8	17.0	4.2	0.4
1972	3.3	15.5	27.0	13.5	11.4	7.2	17.4	4.2	0.4

France (cont.)

A reduction can be seen in the number of new cases of pneumoconiosis, particularly in the coal mines, but the figure remains
relatively high when the reduction in the total workface is taken
into account.

Table 18

New cases of pneumoconiosis - France

	1968	1969	1970	1971	1972
Coal	1 115	1 018	936	859	900
Iron	27	33	17	28	20
Other mines	10	8	5	15	9
Slate pits	8	10	10	22	18
Total "Mines scheme"	1 160	1 069	968	924	947
Quarries in the "General scheme"	23	21	21	11	16

New disability payments effected during the five-year period
are as follows:

1968:   2,880
1969:   2,227
1970:   2,480
1971:   2,093
1972:   2,060

A reduction is also to be noted in these figures which, however,
are not to be compared with the preceding table since some of the
recognised "at work" cases may not be in receipt of an invalidity
payment, while on the other hand, some of the new disability payments may include silicotics recognised only after their retirement.
Furthermore, there may be a delay of a year or more before payments
are finally authorised.

Deaths due to pneumoconiosis are based on figures obtained from
survivors' benefits payments.   They relate only to the "Mines
scheme" and the actual number of deaths would be from 5 to 10 per
cent more than those in table 19.

France (cont.)

Table 19

Deaths from pneumoconiosis - France

Age group	1968	1969	1970	1971	1972
Less than 30	-	-	-	-	-
35-39	3	1	-	-	-
40-44	28	26	21	19	9
45-49	101	85	119	71	55
50-54	93	65	62	73	104
55-59	154	140	169	109	94
60-64	202	191	193	157	139
65-69	178	192	198	149	175
70-74	78	115	112	122	135
75-79	35	42	46	48	46
80 or over	2	2	1	3	4
Total	874	859	921	751	761

The average age of silicotics at death, which in 1958 was
54.6 and in 1967 was 59.5, has evolved as follows:

1968: 60.2
1969: 61.5
1970: 61.0
1971: 62.1
1972: 62.6

Tables 20, 21 and 22 contain further statistics of a general
nature.

Table 20

Percentage of silicotics at work in each age
group (as at 31 December of each year) - France

Age group	1968	1969	1970	1971	1972
Less than 31	0.4	0.2	0.15	0.08	0.05
31-35	5.7	5.1	4.4	3.5	2.5
36-40	21.1	19.0	17.9	15.5	14.7
41-50	69.1	7.21	73.5	75.1	75.0
50 or over	3.7	3.6	4.1	5.8	7.7

France (cont.)

Table 21

Percentage of silicotics at work grouped
according to length of exposure - France

Duration of exposure	1968	1969	1970	1971	1972
Less than 5 years	0.4	0.5	0.4	0.8	0.8
5-9 years	2.2	2.3	2.4	2.5	2.7
10-19 years	34.4	32.7	31.9	31.4	31.7
20-29 "	56.4	56.9	58.5	58.7	58.7
30 years and over	6.6	7.5	6.8	6.6	6.1

Table 22

Silicotics as percentage of total personnel
(surface and underground) - France

	1968	1969	1970	1971	1972
Coal mines excluding Provence	15.64	15.96	15.59	15.09	14.30
Iron mines	1.07	1.24	1.27	1.40	1.52
Other mines	1.18	1.07	1.00	1.10	1.16
Slate pits	2.57	2.55	2.69	2.77	3.23

Germany (F.R.)

The statistics quoted are taken from those of the Mining
Industry Accident Insurance Association together with certain of
those compiled by the Mining Administration.

Medical examinations are carried out for the purpose of determining fitness for employment and for the purposes of placement in
suitable work.   Table 23 shows the number of these examinations
carried out during the five-year period.

Table 23

Pre-employment and periodical medical
examinations - Germany (F.R.)

	1968	1969	1970	1971	1972
Hard coal mining	112 897	112 100	107 352	101 027	81 323
Metal mining	3 482	1 717	2 252	1 486	2 550
Other workings	229	676	519	22	557
Total	116 608	114 493	110 123	102 535	84 430

The decrease in the total number of examinations is related to
the decrease in the total number of persons employed.

Germany (F.R.) (cont.)

In table 24 are shown statistics from the North Rhine-Westphalia mining district relating to the number of exposed persons and their division according to job placement categories. The figures relate to the month of November 1972.

Table 24

Personnel and fitness testing

		Total	Work capacity index				No. of persons examined during the year
			A	B	C	D	
1.	Total above and below ground	158 189	119 272	24 742	12 166	2 009	92 826
	Per cent	100.0	75.4	15.6	7.7	1.3	58.7
1.1	Total underground	116 252	89 080	22 683	4 483	6.0	70 680
	Per cent	100.0	76.6	19.5	3.9		60.8
1.1.1	Miners	106 346	80 926	20 949	4 465	6.0	64.932
	Per cent	100.0	76.1	19.7	4.2		61 1
1.1.2	Officials	9 906	8 154	1 734	18	-	5 748
	Per cent	100.0	82.3	17.5	0.2		58.0
1.2	Total surface	41 937	30 192	2 059	7 683	2 003	22 146
	Per cent	100.0	72.0	4.9	18.3	4.8	52.8
1.2.1	Workers	35 561	24 128	1 923	7 601	1 909	20 005
	Per cent	100.0	67.8	5.4	21.4	5.4	56.3
1.2.2	Officials	6 376	6 064	136	82	94	2 141
	Per cent	100.0	95.1	2.1	1.3	1.5	33.6

Table 25 shows the distribution of personnel by their occupation and their different dust exposure gradings.

Germany (F.R.) (cont.)

Table 25

Dust exposure and personnel - Germany (F.R.)

Type of work	Total workers	Dust exposure grade				Restricted employment personnel
		A	B	C	D	
MINERS -	97 501	52 978	42 395	279	1 849	23 056
1. Stone drivages	2 578	1 871	659	44	4	562
2. Maintenance and prop drawing	8 718	6 111	2 585	-	22	2 065
3. Face preparation and equipping	6 313	3 520	2 691	18	84	1 541
4. Gate road advancing	8 032	3 383	4 393	40	216	1 951
5. Face work, less than 40° dip (total)	26 585	6 376	19 153	96	960	5 248
5.1 Coal getting only	760	141	603	-	16	191
5.2 Coal getting and packing (total)	19 463	2 866	15 684	93	820	3 632
5.2.1 Coal getting and pneumatic stowing	1 105	81	938	-	86	233
5.2.2 Coal getting with caving	18 358	2 785	14 746	93	734	3 399
5.3 Stowing only (total)	589	127	445	-	17	126
5.3.1 Pneumatic	305	57	231	-	17	67
5.3.2 Stowing	284	70	214	-	-	59
5.4 Other work	5 773	3 242	2 421	3	107	1 299
6. Face work, more than 40° dip (total)	2 539	877	1 662	-	-	578
6.1 Coal getting only	1 275	189	1 086	-	-	316
6.2 Coal getting and packing	603	160	443	-	-	105
6.3 Stowing only	265	194	71	-	-	73
6.4 Other work	396	334	62	-	-	84
7 Gate transport and roadway maintenance	13 030	7 381	5 099	55	495	3 571
8 Main haulage	11 981	10 603	1 367	4	7	2 788
9 Other underground work	17 725	12 856	4 786	22	61	4 752
OFFICIALS	9 478	5 209	4 204	17	48	1 556
GRAND TOTAL	106 979	58 187	46 599	296	1 897	24 612

Germany (F.R.) (cont.)

Table 26 shows the total number of persons employed underground.
The figures will not agree with those referring to persons exposed
to dusty conditions, since not all underground are so exposed.

Table 26

Total persons employed underground -
Germany (F.R.)

	1968	1969	1970	1971	1972
Hard-coal mining	167 805	161 951	160 014	158 984	148 826
Metal mining	6 241	5 457	5 255	4 938	4 683
Other mineral working	1 169	1 367	1 302	1 213	1 023
Total	175 215	168 775	166 571	165 135	154 532

Pneumoconiosis statistics

Table 27

Total cases of pneumoconiosis – Germany (F.R.)

	1968			1969			1970			1971			1972		
	Pure silicosis	Silico-tuberculosis	Total	Pure silicosis	Silico-tuberculosis	Total	Pure silicosis	Silico-tuberculosis	Total	Pure silicosis	Silico-tuberculosis	Total	Pure silicosis	Silico-tuberculosis	Total
1	2	3	4	5	6	7	8	9	10	11	12	13	14	15	16
Hard coal mining	39 129	2 003	41 132	37 379	1 939	39 318	35 517	1 880	37 397	33 926	1 834	35 760	32 219	1 742	33 961
Metal mining	1 280	139	1 419	1 180	128	1 308	1 128	122	1 250	1 076	124	1 200	1 023	117	1 140
Other mineral working	106	16	122	128	20	148	126	17	143	110	19	129	139	21	160
Total	40 515	2 158	42 673	38 687	2 087	40 774	36 771	2 019	38 790	35 112	1 977	37 089	33 381	1 880	35 261

Figures shown in tables 27–30 are taken from the records of current compensation payments at the end of each report year compiled by the Mining Industry Mutual Accident Insurance Association (Bergbau-Berufsgenossenschaft).

Table 28

New cases of pneumoconiosis - Germany (F.R.)

	1968			1969			1970			1971			1972		
	Pure sili-cosis	Silico-tuber-culosis	Total	Pure sili-cosis	Silico-tuber-culosis	Total	Pure sili-cosis	Silico-tuber-culosis	Total	Pure sili-cosis	Silico-tuber-culosis	Total	Pure sili-cosis	Silico-tuber-culosis	Total
1	2	3	4	5	6	7	8	9	10	11	12	13	14	15	16
Hard coal mining	920	125	1 045	958	149	1 107	888	111	999	914	145	1 059	856	111	967
Metal mining	65	9	74	33	7	40	40	14	54	33	9	42	34	20	54
Other mineral working	2	1	3	8	3	11	8	1	9	7	4	11	6	-	6
Total	987	135	1 122	999	159	1 158	936	126	1 062	954	158	1 112	896	131	1 027

The figures in table 28 represent cases resulting from exposure during the preceding twelve-month period.

Table 29

Total fatal cases of pneumoconiosis - Germany (F.R.)

	1968			1969			1970			1971			1972		
	Pure sili-cosis	Silico-tuber-culosis	Total	Pure sili-cosis	Silico-tuber-culosis	Total	Pure sili-cosis	Silico-tuber-culosis	Total	Pure sili-cosis	Silico-tuber-culosis	Total	Pure sili-cosis	Silico-tuber-culosis	Total
1	2	3	4	5	6	7	8	9	10	11	12	13	14	15	16
Hard coal mining	1 712	313	2 025	1 773	372	2 145	1 892	312	2 204	1 543	277	1 820	1 468	224	1 692
Metal mining	80	25	105	86	17	103	75	19	94	59	6	65	65	17	82
Other mineral working	5	1	6	10	2	12	6	2	8	10	1	11	3	-	3
Total	1 797	339	2 136	1 869	391	2 260	1 973	333	2 306	1 612	284	1 896	1 536	241	1 777

Table 30

Average dust exposure of silicotics at first
compensation - Germany (F.R.)

	1968		1969		1970		1971		1972	
	Pure silicosis	Silico-tuberculosis	Pure silicosis	Silico-tuberculosis	Pure silicosis	Silico-tuberculosis	Pure silicosis	Silico-tuberculosis	Pure silicosis	Silico-tuberculosis
1	2	3	4	5	6	7	8	9	10	11
Hard coal mining	26.02	23.68	26.01	24.45	26.40	23.13	25.96	24.24	27.43	24.79
Metal mining	19.08	21.44	19.88	21.29	22.88	14.50	23.36	22.00	20.97	20.75
Other mineral working	14.50	22.00	18.25	15.33	23.88	32.00	14.14	9.50	19.50	-

Ghana

The following statistics relate to the Tarkwa and Prestea Gold-fields Limited, subsidiary mines of the State Gold Mining Corporation, based on a report to the District Labour Office.

Number of persons at risk .... more than 5,000

Total of pneumoconiotics
recorded   336

New cases detected and reported   247

Total known deaths from pneumoconiosis   10

Most of the cases reported related to workmen employed underground.

India

The following figures are based on notifications received in the office of the Directorate-General of Mines Safety.

Table 31

Pneumoconiosis statistics - India

	1968	1969	1970	1971	1972
No. of persons exposed to risk:					
- coal mines	236 019	236 626	235 400	228 345	236 523
- metal mines	27 261	27 495	27 014	26 952	28 955
No. of cases of coalminers' pneumoconiosis and silicosis:					
- coal mines	4	3	17	8	3
- metal mines	46	51	47	39	18

Indonesia

No statistics of pneumoconiosis cases are available. The following approximate number of persons at risk are quoted:

Gold mines (underground)   200

Coal mines (underground)   500

Granite quarries   100

Open-pit and other mines   225

Israel

No machinery exists for the compilation of pneumoconiosis statistics.   A few isolated cases of silicosis have come to the attention of the medical authorities.

Malaysia

All cases of pneumoconiosis encountered by registered medical practitioners are required to be reported to the Director-General, Factories and Machinery Department.

The following figures are reported:

Persons exposed to risk 600

Total number of pneumoconiotics   2

Total number of new cases .... Nil

Deaths from pneumoconiosis .... Nil

The above cases were reported among manual workers at crushing plants working on an eight-hour daily exposure.

Morocco

Table 32 gives details of the number of persons at risk in the different mines and the related cases of pneumoconiosis.

As regards coal mines, all underground workers are at risk, the length of exposure varying from 8 to 20 years.

Table 32

Pneumoconiosis statistics – Morocco

Period / Mineral worked	Number of persons exposed to risk						Total number of pneumoconiotics						New cases of pneumoconiotics						Deaths from pneumoconiosis					
	1968	1969	1970	1971	1972	1973	1968	1969	1970	1971	1972	1973	1968	1969	1970	1971	1972	1973	1968	1969	1970	1971	1972	1973
Anthracite	–	806	600	691	–	3 121	142	202	181	185	–	808	–	–	–	–	–	176	–	–	–	–	–	39
Lead-zinc	–	214	642	385	725	1 017	–	9	12	10	10	129	–	7	3	9	5	25	–	–	–	1	1	2
Copper	–	147	–	141	–	150	–	2	–	1	1	–	–	–	–	–	–	–	–	–	–	1	–	–
Manganese	–	–	299	727	255	–	–	–	3	1	1	–	–	–	–	–	–	–	–	–	–	–	–	–
Cobalt	–	–	138	–	248	–	–	9	12	–	–	–	–	–	–	–	–	–	–	–	–	–	–	–
Pyrrbotine	–	–	–	–	–	–	–	–	2	2	–	8	–	–	–	–	–	–	–	–	–	–	–	–

Netherlands

During the period of the present report, the coalmining
industry continued to be run down and a decreasing amount of statistical data became available concerning silicosis.   Some relevant
data provided by the Medical Service of the Netherlands Coal Mines
and the Social Insurance Bank are shown in table 33.

Table 33

Radiographical and other examinations -
Netherlands

	1968	1969	1970	1971	1972
Thorax radiography u/g and surface	19 727	16 382	14 127	11 300	10 530
Thorax radiography large size	5 676	5 906	5 831	4 169	3 639
Examinations for lung function	3 195	2 443	1 935	1 702	1 794
Cardiological examinations	3 705	3 789	3 617	3 611	3 273
Advice in connection with pneumoconiosis	2 116	1 806	1 505	1 335	1 175

New Zealand

Practically no cases of pneumoconiosis are known in New Zealand.
Two cases were recorded in 1957 among some 1,700 coal mine employees
examined.   These have not proved fatal and no deaths have been
recorded.

Norway

Tables 34 and 35 show the number of persons exposed and the
number of new cases registered during the period 1968-1972.

Table 34

Number of persons exposed to silicosis - Norway

	Persons engaged	Employed persons who are believed to be exposed to silicosis
Mines	5 570	3 000
Tunnels	4 000	2 000
Quarries	4 100	2 500

Norway (cont.)

Table 35

New cases of silicosis - Norway

	1968	1969	1970	1971	1972
Mines	8	9	5	7	6
Tunnels	0	3	1	2	0
Quarries	8	2	1	5	0

Peru

The following figures are supplied in connection with pneumo-coniosis:

Number of persons at work (under-ground and surface) .... 50 000 (approx.)

Number of persons exposed to risk 25 168

Total silicosis cases 493

Classified (according to the local classification) as follows:

SI	SII	SIII	STBC	Total
307	138	15	33	493

Other statistics are not available, but it is believed that the average duration of exposure to risk is about five years.

Philippines

There are no recorded cases of pneumoconiosis or silicosis in the mining industry.

Poland

The occupational disease statistics are based on the Ordinances dated 16 July 1968 and 1 December 1969 of the Ministry of Public Health and Social Security.   The Ministry issued an Act concerning pre-employment and periodic medical examinations on 28 April 1968.

Tables 36 and 37 give an idea of the number of workers exposed to the risk of silicosis and of the total number of silicotic sub-jects in chemical mineral mining.

The building materials industry comprised 137 open-cast quarries and five underground mines.   During the period under review, the workforce employed in these undertakings averaged 10,000 people, of whom 770 were technical staff.   The report takes note of six new cases of pneumoconiosis.   The workers concerned were employed at tasks involving no exposure to dust.

Poland (cont.)

Table 36

Total number of persons at risk
by individual mine - Poland

Year	Rudki	Machów	Boguszów	Nowy Lad	Piotrowice	Razem
1968	461	5	60	46	56	628
1969	362	45	65	46	55	573
1970	198	47	63	40	44	392
1971	96	48	64	40	52	300
1972	47	51	67	35	51	251

Table 37

Total number of silicotics by
individual mine - Poland

Year	Rudki	Machów	Boguszów	Nowy Lad	Piotrowice	Razem
1968	7	1	1	-	-	9
1969	2	-	2	-	3	7
1970	3	-	-	1	1	5
1971	2	-	1	-	-	3
1972	-	-	1	-	-	1

Romania

More than 85 per cent of the pneumoconiotics registered in
Romania are from the mining industry.   It is estimated that about
51 per cent of mineworkers are exposed to siliceous dust and most
of these are underground workers, in particular faceworkers and
tunnellers.   The average duration of exposure before the appearance of silicosis during the period in question was about 15 years.

From 1968 to 1972, 32 per cent of the total number of silicotics
was withdrawn from the mining industry, 61 per cent were retired,
7 per cent were given medical attention and 0.7 per cent were fatal.

Table 38 shows the number of new cases together with the total
number of silicotics in coal mines and in mines other than coal.

Romania (cont.)

Table 38

New and total numbers of silicosis cases -
Romania

Year	Total new cases of silicosis %	Total silicotics (%)	
		Coal mines	Mines other than coal
1968	100.0	-	-
1969	94.8	21.9	78.1
1970	100.0	23.6	76.4
1971	80.8	24.6	75.4
1972	56.1	26.3	73.7

Singapore

Tables 39-41 show the number of persons exposed to risk, the new cases, the type of work and the duration of exposure to risk during the years 1968 to 1972.

Table 39

Number of persons exposed and new cases -
Singapore

Year	Number of persons exposed	New cases of pneumoconiosis
1968	1 493	0
1969	1 483	1
1970	1 604	9
1971	1 588	2
1972	1 572	8

Singapore (cont.)

Table 40

Distribution of pneumoconiosis cases in granite
quarries by type of work - Singapore

Job	1968	1969	1970	1971	1972
Odd job	-	-	1	-	1
General worker	-	1	3	-	-
Stone breaker	-	-	-	-	1
Crusher attendant	-	-	3	-	3
Wagon pusher	-	-	-	-	1
Greaser	-	-	1	1	1
Lorry driver	-	-	1	-	-
Driller	-	-	-	1	1
Total	-	1	9	2	8

Table 41

Duration of exposure to risk - Singapore

Year	<5 years	5-10 years	>10 years
1968	0	0	0
1969	0	0	1
1970	0	0	9
1971	1	0	1
1972	0	2	6
Total	1	2	17

Sri Lanka

The incidence of pneumoconiosis is reported as being slight.

Sweden

Following a revision of the basis on which the statistics are
gathered, figures are quoted for the years 1966-1970.

In table 42, it may be assumed that one worker/year corresponds
to 1,950 working hours over the years 1966-1968, 1,850 working hours
for 1969-1970, and for the period 1971-1972, 1,800 working hours for
workers above ground and 1,750 hours for those underground.

Sweden (cont.)

Table 42

Labour employed in mining and quarrying in
1,000 working hours - Sweden

	1966	1967	1968	1969	1970
Mining	27 229	24 778	23 767	23 014	22 966
Quarrying	7 809	7 558	6 761	6 263	6 054

Table 43

Total cases of silicosis (by ten-year periods
according to year of diagnosis) - Sweden

- 1930	1931-40	1941-50	1951-60	1961-70	1971-73
4	319	438	430	436	45

Table 44

Invalidities or deaths compensated,
by year - Sweden

	1967	1968	1969	1970
Mining	16	9	12	16
Tunnelling and rock drilling	4	4	8	5
Quarrying	1	6	2	3

Table 45

Deaths from silicosis, by year - Sweden

	1967	1968	1969	1970
Mining	1	-	1	-
Tunnelling and rock drilling	-	1	2	-
Quarrying	-	1	-	-

Switzerland

Statistics show that 8,620 cases of pneumoconiosis were recognised during the period 1930 to the end of 1972, of which 2,559 have subsequently died.   Among 2,055 cases compensated, 944 died from other causes.   Table 46 indicates the distribution of pneumoconiosis cases during the years 1968-1972.

Table 46

Pneumoconiosis cases during the years
1968-1972 - Switzerland

Industry	Number of cases		Cost in francs		
	Total	%	Total	%	% of cost of industrial accidents
Construction	1 163	69	57 304 639	76	9
Foundries	265	16	8 374 899	11	36
Ceramic industry	61	4	2 815 259	4	30
Masonry and stonecutting	22	1	246 740	0	21
Others	169	10	6 920 303	9	1
Total	1 680	100	75 661 840	100	5

Turkey

Between 65,000 and 70,000 workers are employed in the mines of Zonguldak, of whom about 35,000 work underground.   Table 46 shows the number of pneumoconiotics at work during the years 1965 to 1972.

Table 47

Pneumoconiotics at work - Turkey (Zonguldak)

1965	1966	1967	1968	1969	1970	1971	1972
932	1 060	2 421	2 363	2 347	892	292	215

Table 48 shows the average numbers of workers in dusty occupations at any one time, by work category.

Turkey (cont.)

Table 48

Workers exposed to dust per shift, by work
category - Turkey (Zonguldak)

Category	Approximate number of workers
Supervision	800
Excavation (miners)	3 000
Assistant miners	3 000
Repair work	2 000
Transportation	4 600
Tunnel work in quarries	1 900
Miscellaneous	1 900
Total	18 000

An analysis has been made of the number of cases of pneumoconiosis diagnosed over the years 1952 to 1968, together with the number of microfilm examinations performed.   Before 1954, cases were only recognised after hospitalisation.

Table 49

Numbers of pneumoconiosis cases and examinations
performed, by year - Turkey (Zonguldak)

Year	Pneumoconiosis cases	Microfilm examinations
1952	83	-
1953	160	-
1954	166	10 955
1955	209	1 979
1956	266	2 722
1957	440	1 221
1958	445	5 958
1959	393	9 576
1960	416	-
1961	418	-
1962	463	3 303
1963	477	3 985
1964	557	1 142
1965	825	5 025
1966	1 445	25 788
1967	2 303	n.a.
1968	1 568	n.a.

United Kingdom

Statistics of pneumoconiosis are shown in table 50.

Table 50

Pneumoconiosis statistics - United Kingdom

	1968	1969	1970	1971	1972
Total number of wage earners	38 465	37 137	34 641	33 225	31 422
Total number of pneumoconiotics[a]	1 213	1 138	857	815	n.a.
New cases[b]	22	28	13	14	14
Death from pneumoconiosis[c]	714	716	773	615	618
Other statistics	-	-	-	-	-

[a] total number of disablement payments in other mining and quarrying

[b] in quarrying and mining other than coal mining

[c] in all mining and quarrying - separate figures not available.

United States

The coalmining industry in the United States employs approximately 130,000 workers at over 5,000 mines.   A nationwide study of the prevalence of coalworkers' pneumoconiosis was commenced in 1969 by the US Public Health Service and the US Bureau of Mines. The study included 29 bituminous and 2 anthracite coal mines.   The report from the United States includes a lengthy description of the data obtained from this study, from which tables 51 to 54 have been extracted.   Copies of the full report may be obtained upon request.

United States (cont.)

Table 51

Geographical prevalence of coalworkers' pneumoconiosis
(UICC/Cincinnati 1970 classification) in underground
coalminers, first round of the national study of
coalworkers' pneumoconiosis - United States

Geographical region	Employees examined, number	Category CWP, per cent				
		0[1]	1	2	3	Complicated
Eastern Pennsylvania - (anthracite)	523	40.0	23.3	17.8	4.4	14.5
Central Pennsylvania	455	58.9	21.6	13.4	1.3	4.8
Eastern "	1 006	50.4	36.5	10.9	0.9	1.3
Northern West Virginia	918	70.8	24.7	3.9	0.6	0.0
Southern West Virginia	1 647	72.8	17.2	5.8	0.4	3.8
Virginia	560	71.6	22.8	3.6	0.2	1.8
Ohio	450	68.4	24.7	5.8	0.4	0.7
Kentucky	959	71.0	23.6	3.1	0.2	2.1
Alabama	777	83.3	12.7	2.7	0.1	1.2
Indiana	274	65.3	29.6	4.0	0.0	1.1
Illinois	524	84.9	13.9	1.0	0.0	0.2
Utah	764	86.9	12.2	0.3	0.0	0.6
Colorado	219	95.4	4.6	0.0	0.0	0.0
Total bituminous coals adjusted[2]	8 553	70.0	22.3	5.3	0.4	2.0
Grand total adjusted[2]	9 076	69.4	22.3	5.5	0.5	2.2

[1] No X-ray evidence of CWP.

[2] Totals have been adjusted to account for oversampling in some areas.

United States (cont.)

Table 52

Prevalence of coalworkers' pneumoconiosis in underground
coalminers, medical examinations under the Federal Coal
Mine Health and Safety Act of 1969 - United States

State	Employees examined, number	Category CWP, per cent				
		0[1]	1	2	3	Complicated
Alabama	1 152	88.8	9.0	1.3	0.3	0.6
Arkansas	28	78.5	17.9	-	-	3.6
Colorado	811	96.0	2.5	1.0	0.1	0.4
Illinois	3 957	89.0	8.1	2.0	0.2	0.7
Indiana	162	88.3	7.4	3.7	-	0.6
Iowa	44	97.7	2.3	-	-	-
Kentucky	10 843	91.0	6.8	1.7	0.1	0.4
Maryland	44	79.6	13.6	6.8	-	-
Montana	14	100.0	-	-	-	-
New Mexico	30	83.4	10.0	3.3	3.3	-
Ohio	2 294	94.6	3.8	1.1	-	0.5
Oklahoma	19	94.7	5.3	-	-	-
Pennsylvania - Bituminous coals	13 681	84.2	9.8	4.0	0.3	1.7
Pennsylvania - Anthracite	1 021	67.6	18.5	7.5	0.8	5.6
Tennessee	275	88.0	7.6	4.0	-	0.4
Utah	613	92.3	5.8	1.1	-	0.8
Virginia	4 936	91.1	5.8	2.0	0.2	0.9
Washington	19	100.0	-	-	-	-
West Virginia	21 501	87.1	7.6	3.7	0.3	1.3
Wyoming	36	94.4	2.8	2.8	-	-
Total bituminous coals	60 459	88.2	7.6	2.9	0.2	1.1
Total anthracite and bituminous coals	61 480	87.8	7.8	3.0	0.2	1.2

[1] No X-ray evidence of CWP.

United States (cont.)

Table 53

Average age of underground coalminers, medical examinations
under the Federal Coal Mine Health and Safety Act of 1969
United States

State	Category CWP, per cent				
	0[1]	1	2	3	Compli-cated
Alabama	45.2	54.0	56.7	62.0	56.1
Arkansas	47.4	53.0	-	-	54.0
Colorado	40.0	53.1	57.5	46.0	51.7
Illinois	39.8	52.2	55.3	61.9	59.2
Indiana	47.0	51.5	56.0	-	48.0
Iowa	38.4	61.0	-	-	-
Kentucky	36.1	47.3	51.6	54.3	53.0
Maryland	43.4	54.5	46.7	-	-
Montana	46.4	-	-	-	-
New Mexico	52.8	54.3	50.0	55.0	-
Ohio	32.3	51.8	51.3	41.0	55.5
Oklahoma	32.6	59.0	-	-	-
Pennsylvania - Bituminous coals	41.6	52.9	54.2	54.8	55.7
Pennsylvania - Anthracite	43.9	49.5	51.5	52.3	55.3
Tennessee	37.8	49.1	46.3	-	51.0
Utah	43.8	52.3	52.3	-	55.0
Virginia	32.8	45.6	47.5	52.9	51.7
Washington	53.4	-	-	-	-
West Virginia	36.0	49.3	50.6	49.6	53.2
Wyoming	46.7	53.0	56.0	-	-
Total bituminous coals	37.4	50.2	51.9	52.6	54.3
Total anthracite and bituminous coals	37.5	50.2	51.9	52.6	54.3

[1] No X-ray evidence of CWP.

Table 54

Prevalence of coalworkers' pneumoconiosis in underground coalminers by years of exposure, medical examinations under the Federal Coal Mine Health and Safety Act of 1969 - United States

State	Category CWP, per cent								
	0 [1]			1		2		3	Complicated
	Exposure, Years								
	Less than 1	1-10	Greater than 10	1-10	Greater than 10	1-10	Greater than 10	Greater than 10	Greater than 10
Alabama	3.0	22.9	62.9	0.5	8.5	-	1.3	0.3	0.6
Arkansas	-	21.4	57.1	-	17.9	-	-	-	3.6
Colorado	24.0	28.0	44.0	0.1	2.4	0.1	0.9	0.1	0.4
Illinois	13.7	37.5	37.8	1.2	6.9	0.1	1.9	0.2	0.7
Indiana	6.8	19.8	61.7	1.2	6.2	0.6	3.1	-	0.6
Iowa	4.6	52.2	40.9	-	2.3	-	-	-	-
Kentucky	13.9	36.1	41.0	0.8	6.0	0.1	1.6	0.1	0.4
Maryland	9.1	13.7	56.8	-	13.6	-	6.8	-	-
Montana	-	28.6	71.4	-	-	-	-	-	-
New Mexico	-	10.0	73.4	-	10.0	-	3.3	3.3	-
Ohio	41.7	29.4	23.5	0.4	3.4	0.1	1.0	-	0.5
Oklahoma	21.0	63.2	10.5	-	5.3	-	-	-	-
Pennsylvania - Bituminous coals	16.5	21.2	46.5	0.6	9.2	0.1	3.9	0.3	1.7
Pennsylvania - Anthracite	2.1	17.5	48.0	0.5	18.0	-	7.5	0.8	5.6
Tennessee	2.9	36.4	48.7	0.3	7.3	0.4	3.6	-	0.4
Utah	2.9	32.6	56.8	0.2	5.6	-	1.1	-	0.8
Virginia	19.7	35.6	35.8	0.5	5.3	-	2.0	0.2	0.9
Washington	-	10.5	89.5	-	-	-	-	-	-
West Virginia	20.1	29.2	37.8	0.5	7.1	0.1	3.6	0.3	1.3
Wyoming	13.9	25.0	55.5	-	2.8	-	2.8	-	-
Total bituminous coals	18.0	29.6	40.6	0.6	7.0	0.1	2.8	0.2	1.1
Total anthracite and bituminous coals	17.7	29.4	40.7	0.6	7.2	0.1	2.9	0.2	1.2

1 No X-ray evidence of CWP.

<u>Zambia</u>

Records and reports concerning miners are maintained by the Pneumoconiosis Medical and Research Bureau and the Compensation Board under the Pneumoconiosis Act.

Statistics are shown in table 55.

Table 55

Pneumoconiosis statistics - Zambia

	1968	1969	1970	1971	1972
Number of persons exposed to risk	50 731	57 708	58 262	59 155	Not available
Total number of pneumoconiosis	325+	333+	321+	352+	"
New cases of pneumoconiosis	41	34*	54	33	52
Deaths from pneumoconiosis	NIL NOTIFIED				
Average duration of exposure to risk	in months				
	225	226	225	204	234
Average time since first exposure	285	323	330	294	299
Shortest time of exposure	161	48	50	55	38
Time since first exposure	173	338	413	295	396

* One case was coalminers' pneumoconiosis.

+ Figures for total number of first stage pneumoconiotics not available.

With the exception of the one case of coalminers' pneumoconiosis all cases were silicosis.

PART I

LEGISLATION, ADMINISTRATION, RESEARCH

———————

1. LEGISLATION

Argentina

Recent legislation contains provisions under which technical committees may be set up to study the need for further regulations and to frame the legal texts in certain industries, including mining. As previously reported, Title IX of the Mining Code contains provisions relating to health and safety in mines.

Australia

New legislation introduced during the period under review includes the Mines and Works Regulations Act, 1968-1973 of Tasmania.

Belgium

New legislation includes the enactment of 24 December 1963 concerning occupational diseases and their prevention. Royal decrees include that of 18 January 1964 giving the list of occupational diseases among which are included silicosis, anthraco-silicosis and pulmonary asbestosis with or without pulmonary tuberculosis. The Royal Decree of 16 September 1965 and the Ministerial Decree of 10 December 1970 respectively have set out the appropriate technical measures for dust prevention and suppression underground in coal mines, and that of 10 December 1970 classifies workplaces according to the airborne dust content and prescribes methods for the sampling, measurement and analysis of airborne dust.

Brazil

The following legal texts relate to the prevention and suppression of dust in mining, tunnelling and quarrying:

- the Consolidated Labour Laws, Title II, Cap. V, Section XV, Articles 204, 205, as amended by Decree No. 229 of 28 February 1967, which refer to support, ventilation, illumination, inflammable or explosive gases and to the appointment of qualified shotfirers;

- Ministerial Order No. 491 of 16 September 1965 provides for the grading of workplaces in the mines into three levels according to the health hazard which they may presnet;

- Ministerial Order No. GB 255 of 16 September 1969 sets out standards relating to ventilation and environmental conditions;

- a Decree dated 17 September 1968 providing for the retirement of face-workers after 15 years of service, and for other underground workers after 20 years of service;

Brazil (cont.)

- a Decree dated 6 September 1973 extends the qualifications for
  retirement to various classes of underground mineworkers and
  also provides for the retirement of specified groups of surface
  workers in different occupations including tunnelling and
  quarrying after 25 years of service.

Canada

Recent legislation referred to in the national report includes
the following items:

Manitoba

The Mines Act and Manitoba Regulations 254/73.

Saskatchewan

The following provisions relating to dust prevention and
suppression are included in the Mines Regulation Act, 1971.

Section 59 (1) provides that the ventilations shall ensure a safe
            working environment and that the air shall be free from
            injurious amounts of noxious impurities.

        59 (9) provides for adequate supplies of water under
            pressure where drilling, blasting or other operations
            producing dust take place.

        59 (10) provides for the installation of water sprays in
            development headings.

        59 (11) provides for adequate ventilation in headings over
            a certain length prescribed by an inspector.

Section 279 (1) provides that a positive supply of fresh air shall
            be provided to keep the air free of dust and no person
            shall work or remain where the air contains dust in
            injurious quantities.

       279 (5) provides that any plant where dust accumulates
            shall be regularly cleaned.

       303   provides that the manager of an open pit shall take
            precautions to protect workmen from harmful concentra-
            tions of dust caused by drilling and their dust
            suppression devices are employed.

       330-338 provide for medical examinations for persons work-
            ing in "dust exposure occupations".

Czechoslovakia

Legislative texts that have come into force during the period
covered by the report include:

- No. 42/1970 Sb - Labour Code (section relating to occupational
  safety);

- No. 25/1973 - This measure requires cases of occupational illnesses to be reported to the Ministry of Public Health.

Czechoslovakia (cont.)

Additionally a number of directives have been published by the Mining Administration relating to the protection of health at the working place; these include a prescribed method for the determination of airborne dust, reference HEM - 3441 - 20.8.1970.

East Germany

The following relevant legislative texts were introduced:

- Second administrative regulation under the Decree relating to the notification and compensation of industrial diseases, dated 18.9.68 (Gesetzblatt, Part II, 1968, p. 821).

- Labour and Fire Protection Ordinance 120/2, safety in underground mines (Gesetzblatt, Sonderdruck 767).

- Labour and Fire Protection Ordinance 122/1, safety in open-cast mines, dated 5.10.73 (Gesetzblatt, Sonderdruck 768).

- Labour Protection Ordinance 622/2, prevention of respiratory diseases from non-toxic dusts, dated 13.5.69 (Gesetzblatt, Sonderdruck 627).

- Regulations No. 4 to the Ordinance on Hours of Work and Holidays Ordinance, dated 20.7.67 (Gesetzblatt, Part II, 1967, p. 483).

- DDR Standard TGL 22 311 covering maximum permissible concentrations of non-toxic dust in workplaces.

- Instruction dated 15.3.72 concerning exemptions from DDR occupational health and industrial standards, Ministry of Health Decree No. 6, 1972, p. 36.

- Directive concerning medical aptitude examinations of workers suffering from diseases, illnesses or physical handicaps, in view of their employment on dusty work.

- Directive 035/68 relating to measuring techniques for the control of dust in mines (issued by the Mining Industry Directorate).

- Directive 044/68 setting out the recommended definition for dust control (issued by the "Kammer der Technik").

- Notice relating to the care and treatment of patients with lung diseases (Ministry of Health Decree No. 11, 1969, p. 49).

El Salvador

Regulations relating to safety and health in mining operations were published in July 1971. Certain other provisions which are relevant are to be found in the regulations concerning safety and health in industrial establishments, which were published in February 1971.

Finland

A recent Act relating to the supervision of labour protection
(No. 131/73) makes provision for inspection of industrial establishments and includes provisions relating to dust prevention in mines
and quarries.   A Decree of the Council of State (No. 637/71) makes
provision for pre-assignment and periodic medical examination of
persons working in occupations involving harmful dust exposures.

France

Relevant legislation in force was listed in the third report
of the present series.

Germany (F.R.)

A number of legislative texts were introduced during the period
covered by the report.   These are listed by region:

-   Baden Württemburg: Technical Directive of 24 August 1971 con-
    cerning the prevention and suppression of harmful silicogenic
    dust underground and on surface (paragraphs 292-299 of the
    General Mining Ordinance).

-   Hesse: Directive by the Divisional Mining Office of 6 June
    1969 relating to pre-employment and periodic medical examina-
    tions (paragraphs 20 and 21 of the General Mining Ordinance).

-   Hesse: Technical Directive by the Divisional Mining Office of
    6 June 1969 concerning the prevention and suppression of harm-
    ful silicogenic dust underground and on surface (paragraph 22
    of the General Mining Ordinance).

-   Nordrhein-Westfalen: Decree by the Divisional Mining Director-
    ate for Coal Mines of 18 December 1970 and 20 February 1970
    (paragraphs 17-24).

-   Nordrhein-Estfalen: Decree by the Divisional Mining Director-
    ate for Metal Mines, Salt Mines and Quarrying of 18 December
    1970 and 20 February 1970 (paragraphs 18-20).

-   Nordrhein-Westfalen: Instructions from the Divisional Mining
    Directorate relating to the interpretation of the results of
    dust measurements made in terms of the regulations.

-   Nordrhein-Westfalen: Directive by the Divisional Mining Office
    relating to the use of coal-seam infusion dated 1 September
    1972.

-   Saarland and Rheinland-Pfalz: Directive by the Divisional
    Mining Office dated 14 June 1968 concerning routine dust
    measurement in coal mines.

-   Saarland and Rheinland-Pfalz: Directive by the Divisional
    Mining Office dated 7 July 1970 concerning pre-employment and
    periodic medical examinations.

-   Saarland and Rheinland-Pfalz: Instructions from the Divis-
    ional Mining Directorate dated 1 December 1972 concerning the
    introduction of gravimetric dust measurement.

Ghana

Part 11 of the "Mining Regulations, 1970" relates to ventilation and dust prevention.

Greece

Regulations relating to work in mines and quarries were issued under Ministerial Decree dated 16 August 1972.

Guatemala

Decree No. 342 of the Mines Code and No. 47-69 of the law relating to quarries are at present in force. Technical standards relating to the prevention and suppression of dust are not however provided for, since it is considered that this problem is not encountered as water is used in all drilling operations and dust and gases resulting from blasting operations are eliminated by ventilation during a compulsory one-hour interval at the end of each shift.

Honduras

Regulations relating to safety, health and hygiene in the mining and metallurgical industries came into force on 27 September 1971. Applicable to all mining operations, including the transport and treatment of minerals and the construction of tunnels, Chapter IX contains provisions relating to the prevention of dust in underground workings.

India

Regulation 123 of the Coal Mines Regulations, 1957 and Regulation 124 of the Coal Mines Regulations, 1961 relate to precautions against dust in all underground operations. These provisions relate, inter alia, to the design and arrangements for picks on coal-cutting machines, the use of water sprays and jets, the installation of exhaust ventilation and to general measures for dust control.

Israel

The "Safety at Work Ordinance (New Version) 1970" includes legislation covering the safety and health of workers in atmospheres where dangerous dust is produced and which applies to mines and quarries.

Jamaica

Chapter 253 (Section 61) of the Mining Law provides for the Commissioner of Mines to act in cases where there is a health hazard due to the working or processing of minerals on a mining or prospecting lease. No specific government instructions or codes of practice exist in respect of dust.

Malagasy Republic

Legislation covering this subject is in course of preparation.

Malawi

Legislation relating to dust prevention in underground workings is included in the "Explosive Regulations" and in the "Mining
(Safety) Regulations".

Mexico

The new Federal Labour Law, in Articles 513 and 514, relates
to pneumoconiosis and pulmonary diseases, which are included in
the list of diseases recognised as being of occupational origin.
Further references to the prevention and suppression of dust are
quoted in Article 37, Annexes 2 and 3 of the regulations relating
to occupational health, and in Articles 149, 150 and 249 of the
mine safety regulations.

Morocco

Legislation regarding medical prevention, periodic X-ray
examinations, and duties of occupational physicians and safety and
health officers has been in force since 1947.   A number of modifications were made and definitions added in 1960 with respect to the
status of mineworkers and the specific measures of medical prevention.

Netherlands

The latest regulations (Mining Regulations 1964) provide for
the establishment of dust concentration limits and for the appointment of an official to take charge of dust sampling and analysis in
respect of conditions at each working place.   Four categories are
established in respect of which the action required to be taken is
laid down.

New Zealand

The Mining Act 1926 and Regulations have been replaced by the
Mining Act 1971 and Mining (Safety) Regulations 1973.

Norway

A new Act concerning mines, No. 70 of 30 June 1972, came into
effect on 1 April 1973.   The Act relating to the protection of
workers, with certain modifications, was enforced in respect of
Svalbard (Spitsbergen).   A guide to the ventilation of mines is
in course of preparation.

Pakistan

Amendments to the Mines Act 1923 which were issued in June 1973 included provisions on occupational and on the furnishing of relevant statistical information by mining companies. Further provisions vest powers in the Government to frame regulations dealing with problems arising from airborne dust.

Panama

Provisions relative to the protection of workers are to be found in the Labour Code. However, since no mining operations are carried out which give rise to a dust hazard, such legislation has not been included among the foregoing provisions.

Peru

New safety and health regulations for the mining industry were introduced and came into force from August 1973. Provisions included relate to ventilation requirements and to special requirements in the case of coal mines. Medical and X-ray examinations of persons exposed to dust are required.

Philippines

The prevention and suppression of dust in mining, tunnelling and quarrying is governed by the Mines Safety Rules under the Act No. 104.

Poland

Training of mineworkers has been organised in accordance with the decree of the Ministry of Chemical Mineral Mining of 1 April 1967.

Romania

The legislation relating to the prevention and suppression of silicogenic dust is to be found among the standards laid down for occupational safety in industry generally together with the special labour protection standards enforced in the mining industry. Permissible limits for various dusts are set out in the following table.

Romania (cont.)

Table 56

Permissible limits for airborne dusts –
Romania

	Type of dust	Permissible limits mg/m^3
1	Dust containing more than 70 per cent SiO_2	1
2	" " from 70 to 40 " " "	2
3	" " " 40 to 10 " " "	4
4	" " less than 10 " " "	8
5	Amorphous silica dusts (diatomaceous earth, etc.)	4
6	Synthetic abrasive dusts (carborundum, etc.)	5
7	Silicate dusts:	
	- asbestos dust with more than 10 per cent fibrous silicate (chrysotile tremolite, etc.)	2
	- other silicate dusts (mica, talc, kaolin, etc.)	4
	- cement dust	15
8	Coal dust	10
9	Cotton, linseed, hemp, tobacco and tea dusts	4
10	Other dust	15

By Order No. 1010/1970 of the Ministry of Mines, Petroleum and
Geology, the "assignments and working procedures of the Consultative
Technical and Scientific Commission for Pneumoconiosis Laboratories"
were approved in 1970. Furthermore, a number of regulations and
recommendations concerning technical, preventive and medical measures for the control of harmful substances, occupational accidents
and diseases have entered into force.

The Technical and Scientific Commission for Pneumoconiosis
Prevention and Dust Control began its work in 1967. The Commission's main task consists in elaborating a standard policy in this
field; it directs and superintends the activities of the pneumoconiosis laboratories set up to solve the problems submitted to them
by the mines in their respective districts.

Singapore

Sand and granite quarries operations are governed by the Sand
and Granite Quarries Act, 1971 and the related Regulations.
Section 54 of the Factories Act, 1973, requires all practical measures to be taken to protect employed persons against inhalation of
dust or fumes.

Sweden

Reference is made to the Workers' Protection Act and Workers' Protection Ordinance, 1974.

Other directives or instructions related to the present report include:

- Instructions of the National Swedish Board of Occupational Safety and Health ... SFS 1972:1964.
- Ditto   ... SFS 1973:846.
- Instructions of the Industrial Safety Inspectorate ... ... SFS 1973:847.

- Bulletin of the National Swedish Board of Occupational Safety and Health ... Nos. 72.2, 71.4, 72.6, 71.7, 70.6.

- Instructions published by the National Swedish Board of Occupational Safety and Health relating to: respiratory precautions (Nos. 45:4, 70:6); rock drilling (No. 67); and quarrying (No. 75).

Switzerland

A new Law concerning occupational diseases was approved on 17 December 1973 by the competent authority.

Turkey

Legislation introduced during the period under consideration included an Act (No. 1475) entitled "Labour Act", adopted on 25 May 1971. A number of new regulations were introduced: these included No. 7/5735 of 31 January 1973 relating to the restriction of working hours in certain job categories; No. 7/5835 of 12 February 1973 on the same subject; No. 7/7583 of 4 December 1973 relating to occupational safety and health; and No. 7/6174 of 4 September 1973 relating to arduous and dangerous jobs.

United Arab Republic

Relevant legislation is to be found in the Labour Law (No. 91 of 1959, Articles 142-145, 150-155, 220, 226, 227). Ministerial Orders Nos. 157 and 158 of 25 August 1959 relate to medical examination of workers in mining and quarrying and to first aid, while No. 195 of 29 October 1959 relates to safety in mining and quarrying.

United Kingdom

The principal legislation consists of the Mines and Quarries Act 1954 to 1971 as supplemented or amended by regulations made under the Health and Safety at Work Act, 1974. Legislation was in course of preparation dealing specifically with the problem of respirable dust in coal mines and will deal with methods to be used to reduce the amount of respirable dust entering the mine air, method and frequency of sampling, and the setting of permitted levels of dust concentrations including the proportion of quartz. They will also provide for increased medical supervision of men exposed to dust.

United States

The Federal Coal Mine Health and Safety Act of 1969 (Coal Act)
(PL 91-173) expanded greatly the scope of previous federal laws and
regulations.   It established many new mandatory safety standards
for underground coal mines.   Its requirements for safety in the
mines are detailed and specific.   They deal with roof control,
ventilation, rock dusting, electrical equipment, blasting and
explosives, hoisting and man trips, escapeways, fire protection,
emergency shelters, communication and many other safety measures.

For the first time, a federal law established mandatory health
standards.   The mandatory health standards required mine-operators,
within six months after enactment of the Coal Act, to maintain a
level of 3.0 milligrams or less of respirable dust per cubic metre
of air (mg/m^3).   The Coal Act also specified that this level be
reduced to 2.0 milligrams or less per cubic metre of air after
30 December 1972.

As for the individual coalminer's health, the Coal Act provides
that each miner shall be given the opportunity to have chest X-rays
both at the beginning of his employment and at specified intervals
thereafter.   Upon evidence of the development of coalworkers'
pneumoconiosis, the miner has been given the right to transfer,
without loss in pay, to an area of the mine where the concentration
of respirable dust is not more than 2.0 milligrams per cubic metre
(mg/m^3) when the 3.0 mg/m^3 standard is in effect, and not more than
1.0 mg/m^3 when the 2.0 mg/m^3 standard is in effect.   When the
applicable concentration of respirable dust cannot be achieved, the
individual has the right to be transferred to that area where the
concentration of respirable dust is the lowest obtainable below
2.0 mg/m^3.

The Coal Act also specifies that every underground coal mine
in the United States must have a minimum of four health and safety
inspections each year by federal coal mine inspectors.   Furthermore,
it permits a representative of the mineworkers to obtain an immed-
iate inspection of any mine when there is reason to believe the mine
environment constitutes a hazard.

In addition to its enforcement provisions, the Coal Act author-
ises an expansion of the Bureau of Mines health and safety research
and education and training programmes.   Mine operators are required
to train and retrain mineworkers in first-aid and good safety
practices through programmes approved by the Secretary of the
Interior.   Mandatory reporting is required by mine operators of
all accidents, whether or not they cause fatalities or personal
injuries.

The Coal Act provides for the assessment of civil and/or
criminal penalties for violations of standards.   Mine operators may
be assessed civil penalties up to $25,000.   Miners may be fined up
to $250 for smoking, carrying smoking materials, matches, or
lighters underground.

To grant the mining industry sufficient time to comply with
the stringent requirements with respect to the respirable dust
standards and electric face equipment, the Coal Act established an
Interim Compliance Panel whose main function is to grant waivers in
instances where delays are justified.

United States (cont.)

The Coal Act also provides grants under certain conditions to States to train inspectors and to expedite Federal-State co-operation as well as to maximise the effectiveness of inspection force. However, the Coal Act contains no authorisation for the Secretary of Interior to delegate any of his authority and responsibility to the States.

Another major requirement of the Coal Act is the development and publication of proposed mandatory health and safety standards for surface coal mines and for surface work areas of underground coal mines. On 22 May 1971, the mandatory safety standards - surface coal mines and surface work areas of underground coal mines became effective. The mandatory health standards became effective on 30 June 1972.

USSR

Rules and instructions designed to ensure that airborne dust contents in the mines be kept within the permitted standards are set out in the "Safety Regulations for Work in Coal and Schistose Coal Mines" (Moscow, Nedra, 1973), and "Guidelines for Dust Prevention in Coal Mines" (Moscow, Nedra, 1971).

Venezuela

The Ministry of Public Works, in a directive dated 14 October 1974, has set out requirements to be observed during tunnelling operations for the prevention of dust. These requirements relate to ventilation requirements and to the use of water.

Vietnam

In Chapter XI of the Labour Code dealing with the health and safety of workers, special dispositions are included in Section III which relate to mines and quarries. Decree No. 197-BLD/TTT/ND, dated 23 September 1968 sets out standards to be observed in the case of those employed in public works and in the construction industry and requires employers to take measures to protect the health of the workers. These measures include prevention of dust, fumes and gases in the working place and the provision of personal protective equipment where this is not practicable.

Zambia

The Mining Regulations, 1971 contain in Part IX extensive provisions relating to ventilation and the related underground conditions and empower the Chief Inspector of Mines to prescribe maximum levels for gas, fume or dust content in the general body of the mine air. Further provisions relate to the use of diesel units underground, to the supply and use of water for dust suppression and in drilling, to precautions to be taken when blasting, and to the removal, control or disposal of dust at tipping stations and other points underground.

2. ADMINISTRATION

Information relating to the name, scope and similar details
concerning the competent authorities has not been included in the
present summary.   Available information, which has in most cases
appeared in previous International Reports on the prevention and
suppression of dust in mining, tunnelling and quarrying, will be
supplied on request.

3. RESEARCH

In providing their national reports on recent research in the
field of dust prevention and related matters, many governments have
furnished technical reports, reprints and other documents relating
to the subjects mentioned.   Although not included in the present
summary, copies of such reports may be made available to interested
persons upon request.

Australia

The Joint Coal Board's Standing Committee on Dust Research and
Control continued its work on dust in coal mine atmospheres.
Figures provided relating to dust concentrations indicate that airborne dust concentrations in the coal mines of New South Wales have
been maintained at satisfactory levels in spite of a considerable
increase in the use of mechanical units for the production of coal.
Following the holding of the First Australian Pneumoconiosis
Conference in 1968, the proceedings were published together with a
number of further studies relating to airborne dust problems.

Canada

The Mines Branch Mining Research Centre of the Department of
Energy, Mines and Resources, Ontario, established an Environmental
Control Group in 1960.   The prime objective of the programme of
this group is to improve the quality of mine air.   During the
period 1968 to 1972, work was undertaken in the fields of respirable
dust, radioactive dust, noise, spontaneous combustion, methane
emission and combustion products from explosives.

It was reported that a study of miners' and foundrymen's lung
functions was in progress in the province of Manitoba.

Czechoslovakia

Recent investigations have been directed towards obtaining
greater precision in the measurement of airborne dust, both in
sampling and in measurement and analysis.   Further work was concerned with the development of pneumoconiosis and aimed at obtaining
more precise criteria for the diagnosis, examination and prognosis
of illness among pneumoconiotics.   Results of this work have been
published.

Czechoslovakia (cont.)

Progress is reported in the following fields of activity:

(a) Coal mines -

- statistical and mathematical evaluation of the influence of technological factors on dust concentrations at the working place;

- the relationship between dust concentrations and the onset of pneumoconiosis;

- development and testing of dust monitoring devices (types DP-50 and DP-20);

- development of new-type filters for dust sampling (TAFPC);

- long hole face infusion techniques;

- the use of water and foam in conjunction with coalgetting machines;

- the use of foam in drilling;

- consolidation of dust in roadways, etc.;

- improved-type dust respirator (R-E4).

(b) Metal mines -

- study of the fibrogenic characteristics of different forms of SiO_2;

- study of the properties of different mine dusts;

- study of aerosols in suspension in mine air;

- experimental investigations of the relationship between particle size of dust and the development of silicosis;

- techniques for automatic recording of airborne dust concentrations.

East Germany

The following institutes are engaged in work relating to silicosis in the mining industry:

- Zentralinstitut für Arbeitsmedizin der Deutschen Demokratischen Republik (ZAM), Berlin: this institute carries on research into, inter alia, dust prevention and lung diseases and is responsible for working out MAC values for non-toxic dusts;

- Institut für Bergbausicherheit, Leipzig: this institute provides the technical background for the State inspection services.

East Germany (cont.)

Recent progress in research has included the development of a gravimetric-type dust measuring instrument. The instrument uses a cyclone-type elutriator to eliminate large particles in accordance with the "Los-Alamos" curve. Fine particles are collected on an electrically activated membrane having an extremely low resistance to air flow. Known as Types SPG 10 and 20, these instruments have a capacity for 10 m^3/h and 20 m^3/h respectively.

France

Research in France is reported under three headings: CERCHAR (Centre for Study and Research of the French Coalmining Industry); CEMM (Centre for Mining Medical Studies at Sin-le-Noble); and the Technical Service of the Chamber of French Iron Mines.

1. CERCHAR: Studies under way during the period 1968-1972 included the following:

Water infusion in narrow seams - recent studies tend to show that the infusion may be even more effective with a reduced quantity and pressure of water and that the aim should be to impregnate the coal with water and not to inject it. The methods of operation are described.

Water infusion in wide seams - exploitation of wide seams is now commonly performed by a type of shrinkage mining (soutirage) which, however, unless precautions are taken may lead to a deterioration in the airborne dust concentrations in the workplaces. The application of water infusion from the roadways has been studied in these cases and it has been found necessary to introduce large quantities (10 to 15 per cent water in relation to the volume of coal in situ) in order to compensate for loss by leakage and by evaporation. It has been found necessary to maintain a continual flow of water, even on non-working days, and precautions have been introduced to avoid accidental leakage.

A further dust problem that has arisen in connection with type of working has been the creation of large dust clouds when powered supports are being advanced. Steel mesh sheets, used to maintain the roof, are covered with sheets of plastic material to form a screen which prevents the dust from falling and also enable drawpoints to be created where water may be applied to prevent airborne dust formation. The plastic sheets also serve to protect the personnel from dripping of the water used for infusion.

Among devices used for dust collection, mention is made of a venturi-type wet dust collector which may be mounted on a mining machine or used in conjunction with a secondary ventilation column.

A mathematical analysis of the spread of the water in infused panels has enabled deductions to be drawn relating to the influence on the humidity of the coal of the dip, the effect of fissures, etc. This has enabled improved patterns of infusion to be introduced.

Laboratory experiments on the use of wetting agents were continued with a view to making more effective use of water for dust suppression and for infusion of the coal body.

France (cont.)

A new device for measuring respirable dust underground was reported.   Described as the CPM 3, its principal characteristics include a rotating filter made of polyurethane foam for capturing the dust particles;   a cyclone-type elutriator designed to eliminate the larger particles;   a sampling rate of 3 m^3/hour and weighing 2,500 kg.   It is intrinsically safe.

Studies carried out in relation to the "dust index" used in France for some 20 years have shown that the risk of pneumoconiosis is related more to the presence of dusts of various types rather than to the presence of quartz alone.   On this basis a new approach has been made to the question of setting permissible limits for dust concentrations with the introduction of a "reference dust level". This factor provides a basis for the classification of working places according to their dustiness and can also provide guidance for the placement of personnel.

2.   CEMM: Very little new research is reported from this centre.   A number of new publications and communications were prepared.

3.   Technical Service of the Chamber of French Iron Mines: Work during this period concentrated on the improvement of ventilation.   A technique using an air curtain through which it is found that dust will not pass has been developed.   Wide hole drilling has been introduced as an aid to providing additional ventilation upcast or downcast in the mines.   From 2.4 m up to 3.6 m in diameter such shafts have been cut up to 240 m in depth.

New work has been effected on dust prevention in drilling and in roof bolting and experiments have been made both with dry drilling using dust collectors and with new methods for wet drilling. The former were abandoned because of the low efficiencies achieved and because of the cumbersome nature of the equipment.

Germany (F.R.)

Research institutes that are involved in work relating to the prevention of silicosis and in dust prevention are named in the following list.   Relevant publications and technical studies emanating from these institutes are to be found in the bibliographical list.

Institutes engaged in work relating to silicosis in the mining industry:

- Lehrstuhl für experimentelle Chirurgie der Universität - Köln-Linderthal (Prof. Dr. Bretschneider);

- Berufsgenossenschaftliche Krankenanstalten "Bergmannsheil Bochum" - Bochum (Prof. Dr. Fritze);

- Pathologisches Institut der Universität - Münster (Prof. Dr. Giese);

- Medizinische Klinik und Poliklinik der Westf. Wilhelms-Universität - Münster (Prof. Dr. Hauss);

Germany (F.R.) (cont.)

- Institut für Hygiene und Arbeitsmedizin - Klinikum Essen der
  Universität - Essen (Prof. Dr. Klosterkötter);

- Pharmakologisches Institut der Universität - Gottingen
  (Prof. Dr. Lendle);

- Physiologisches Institut der Universität - Dusseldorf
  (Prof. Dr. Lochner);

- Electronenmikroskopische Abteilung am Pathologischen Institut
  der Universität - Heidelberg (Dr. Nemetschek);

- Staatsinstitut für Staublungenforschung und Gewerbe-hygiene
  beim Hygiene-Institute der Westf. Wilhelms-Universität -
  Münster (Prof. Dr. Reploh);

- Med. Institut für Lufthygiene und Silokoseforschung an der
  Universität - Düsseldorf (Prof. Dr. Schlipköter);

- Max-Planck-Institut für experimentelle Medizin - Göttingen
  (Prof. Dr. Schoedel);

- Abteilung für Pathologie der Med. Fakultät an der Rhein -
  Westf. Techn. Hochschule - Aachen (Prof. Dr. Schoenmackers);

- Forschungsabteilung für Elektronenmikroscopie der Freien
  Universität Berlin - Berlin-Dahlem (Prof. Dr. Schwarz);

- Physiologisches Institut der Johannes Gutenberg-Universität -
  Mainz (Prof. Dr. Thews);

- Krankenhaus Bethanien - Moers (Prof. Dr. Worth).

     It is also noted that the Arbeitsgemeinschaft des Saarlandes
für Silikoseforschung und Silikoseverhüting, (Joint Association of
the Saar for Silicosis Research and Silicosis Prevention), is now
to be known as Arbeitsgemeinschaft des Saarlandes zur Erforschung
und Verhüting von Silikose und Lärmschäden, thereby adding the
problems of injury due to noise to the research and prevention programmes of this association.

India

     The Central Mining Research Station at Dhanbad recently con-
ducted a survey covering 8,822 coalminers in conjunction with the
Rajendra Memorial Research Institute of Medical Sciences whose
findings indicated the incidence of pneumoconiosis to be
10.8.per cent.   Very little correlation could be effected between
the prevalence of pneumoconiosis and the dust counts.   A previous
survey had revealed an incidence of 18.8 per cent.

Netherlands

     The results of the study on dust prevention in the Dutch coal
mines (referred to in the Fourth International Report) were published
by the Netherlands Central Organisation for Applied Scientific
Research (Publication No. 306, by Dr. F. Hartogensis, February 1968).

Netherlands (cont.)

More recent research related to the quartz content of the dust (1969), quartz content and the size of dust particles (1968), quartz content, size of dust particles and the gas content of the dust (1970). Full reports on these investigations are contained in the annual reports of the Dust Institute in Limburg for the years mentioned.

Poland

The Institute of Occupational Medicine, the Central Laboratory of Occupational Medicine and the scientific departments of plants in the chemical-mineral mining industry have co-ordinated their study programmes and conducted research into the following problems:

- purification of the air penetrating into the operator's cabs of mining machines;

- dust suppression during sulphur mineral mining;

- dust exposure of sulphur ore miners;

- criteria for the exposure to sulphur ore dust.

Romania

The central scientific organisation concerned with mining safety and health problems is the Mine Safety Research Centre at Petrosani. There are in addition three institutes concerned with coal mines, lignite mines and non-ferrous mining and metallurgy. Occupational safety and health in mines is also the concern of four institutes working in the field of public health and general occupational health.

Singapore

The Singapore Institute of Standards and Industrial Research conducted research on a dust control system appropriate to local conditions.

Sweden

The National Swedish Board of Occupational Safety and Health and the Institute for Industrial Medicine, the National Road Administration, the Mining Research Foundation of the Swedish Mine-owners' Association, the Institute for Mineral Processing at the Royal Instiute of Technology, the Foundation for Safety and Health in the Construction Industry and the Committee for Workers' Protection are all associated in research relevant to the mining sector. Mention may be made of the "Silicosis project" - an industry-by-industry evaluation of the silicosis risk, which has been in progress over the period under consideration.

Switzerland

Studies relating to the quality of the air in large tunnels and to ventilation systems were made by a working group on the ventilation of tunnels during construction during the period covered by the present report. A final report was published in 1970.

United Arab Republic

The following institutes are engaged in relevant research:

- the National Institute of Research;

- the National Institute of Occupational Safety and Health;

- the University Colleges of Medicine, of Engineering and of Science.

United Kingdom

The Safety in Mines Research Establishment (SMRE) is now part of the Health and Safety Executive.

The mining-oriented establishments of the NCB (Mining Research Establishment and Central Engineering Establishment) have been merged to form the unified Mining Research and Development Establishment at Stanhope Bretby, Burton-upon-Trent, Staffordshire.

Since the last report, SMRE has completed its programme of research on the amount and composition of dust found in the lungs of coalminers after death.   This work was a contribution to a joint research project, carried out in co-operation with the Pneumoconiosis Research Unit of the Medical Research Council, on the relation between lung dust and X-ray category in simple pneumoconiosis.   Work in this field is now being carried out by the Institute of Occupational Medicine.

SMRE's work on the pneumoconiosis hazard is now principally concerned with instruments for measuring respirable dust concentrations and with methods of personal protection against harmful dusts. The personal gravimetric dust-sampling instrument (SIMPEDS) mentioned in the last report is now being manufactured commercially and underground trials are being carried out in the UK and in West Germany.   Another version of this instrument, known as SIMQUADS, has been designed for use in quarries and other industries where a cap lamp and battery are not worn.   Weighing 1 kg, this instrument is fitted with a cyclone elutriator/filter unit which can be attached to the wearer's clothing or used as a fixed-point sampler. Based on the existing prototypes, no difficulty is anticipated in producing a commercial version.

Further research has been carried out on the scattering and absorption of light by dust of respirable size.   Based on this research, a new dust-sampling instrument has been designed to provide an instantaneous indication and continuous record of the surface-area concentration of respirable-size airborne dust. Using a beam of near infra-red radiation it has a response which is substantially independent of particle refractive index, so that the accuracy of the estimate of surface-area concentration is not

United Kingdom (cont.)

affected by changes in the composition of the dust cloud.   Known as
SIMSLIN for use in coal mines, it weighs 16 kg and it is expected
that it will be particularly useful for dust control and dust
suppression research.

A respirator has been developed in the form of a helmet, for
protecting men working in dusty atmospheres.   A small fan at the
back of the helmet blows dusty air through a filter in the top of
the helmet so that clean filtered air passes downwards between a
transparent visor and the wearer's face.   Ingress of dusty air is
reduced by means of a flexible skirt at the bottom of the helmet,
while a less cumbersome version for use in mines makes use of plastic
foam sealing.   The fan delivers about 200 litres/minute and may be
driven from a cap lamp battery.   Underground tests are being carried
out.

Much of the research mentioned in the previous report is now
being implemented in terms of practical machines and devices, and
recent work has been directed towards these engineering applications.
Items of research and development that may be mentioned include the
following:

- nucleonic steering devices for keeping the power-loader in
  the seam;

- more rational design of picks and cutting heads;

- studies are being made on the loading action of shearer drums
  on a versatile 1/8 scale model so as to obtain information on
  optimum loading speeds, vane helix angle, etc.;

- pick face flushing on power-loaders is now being fully implemented;

- the best use of water sprays for reducing make of dust on
  conveyors;

- studies are being made on the introduction of air and water
  to the vicinity of the cut through the shaft of the shearer
  to combat dust and methane: water-powered air movers are
  also being used to trap dust released into the air when
  powered supports are lowered, and for incorporation in the
  cowls of drum shearers;

- new dust extraction techniques have been studied for use in
  roadways, with particular regard to the "overlap" system:
  certain new materials hold promise as excellent filters;

- to meet possible new legislation relating to more stringent
  examination of mineworkings, the NCB gravimetric sampler
  Type 113A has been modified so that it can record automatically
  on five successive shifts.

United States

Mining research is under the responsibility of the Department
of the Interior through the Director, Bureau of Mines.

United States (cont.)

Mining research is conducted at five centres:

- Denver Mining Research Centre;
- Environmental Affairs Field Office;
- Pittsburgh Mining and Safety Research Centre;
- Spokane Mining Research Centre;
- Twin Cities Mining Research Centre.

The coal mine health and safety programme is divided administratively into ten categories. Funding allocated to each of the respective categories is shown in figure 1.

With regard to respirable dust, the objective and major study areas are represented in figure 2.

The greater part of the expenditure on dust research during fiscal year 1972 was allocated to the funding of contractual agreements and grants, thereby making use of expertise available in industry, universities and other government agencies. A compilation of all health research funding is published annually in the Secretary of Interior's metal and non-metal and coal reports.

In 1972, 20 projects were nominated under the Bureau of Mines programme to transfer experimental results into practical application that would or could have a useful impact on the coal industry.

USSR

Research in the USSR relates to the following:

- control of dust in fissures within the coal face;

- reduction of dust created by crushing of the coal seam and adjacent strata;

- elimination of airborne dust in the mine air;

- individual protective equipment;

- improvement of duct control techniques;

- the prevention and treatment of pneumoconiosis.

Zambia

The Research Laboratory of the Mines Safety Department and the Pneumoconiosis Medical and Research Bureau are engaged in a study on the relationship between inhaled dust and the incidence of silicosis.

United States (cont.)

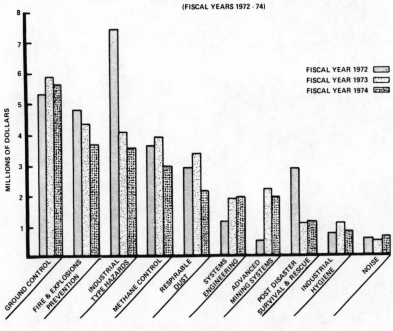

ALLOCATION OF RESEARCH FUNDS
(FISCAL YEARS 1972 - 74)

Figure 1

United States - Allocation of research funds

RESPIRABLE DUST

OBJECTIVE:

PROVIDE IMPROVED EQUIPMENT AND
TECHNIQUES FOR PROTECTING MINERS
FROM EXPOSURE TO RESPIRABLE COAL
MINE DUST.

STUDY AREAS:

● DUST FORMATION
● DUST CONTROL
● DUST MEASUREMENT

APPLICATION OF RESULTS:

● 1971 1972: WATER INFUSION OF COAL BEDS FOR
   CONTROL OF RESPIRABLE DUST DEMONSTRATED
   UNDERGROUND AT EASTERN ASSOCIATED
   COAL CORP'S FEDERAL NO. 2 MINE.

● 1972: WATER-BASED HIGH-EXPANSION FOAMING
   SYSTEM USED WITH A CONTINUOUS MINER TO
   REDUCE DUST AT FACE IN PITTSBURGH
   COAL CO'S MATHIES MINE.

● 1972: FOAM SYSTEM FOR DUST SUPPRESSION
   ON CONVEYORS AND TRANSFER POINTS
   DEMONSTRATED AT HANNA COAL CO'S
   ROSE VALLEY MINE.

● 1972: PROTOTYPE DUST METERS USED AT
   BETHLEHEM STEEL CO'S CAMBRIA SLOPE
   NO. 33 MINE.

● 1973: NEW WATER-FLUSHED BIT DESIGN
   DEMONSTRATED UNDERGROUND AT U.S. STEEL
   ROBENA NO. 1 MINE.

Figure 2

United States - Research on respirable dust

PART II

DUST PREVENTION AND SUPPRESSION PRACTICES

————————

For purposes of the present summary, sub-sections 1 to 18 of
Part II, as classified in the original plan for national reports
presented at the 1955 Meeting of Experts, have been consolidated
under the headings of the respective countries.

Argentina

Considerable progress has been made towards the general use
of water for dust prevention purposes in mines underground.
Standards have been laid down by the competent authority relating
to atomisers or spray nozzles which include details for their
characteristics, construction and methods of use.   While conditions in the larger mining operations are in many respects more
satisfactory, it is in the small mines that many difficulties
exist in relation to efforts to improve the working environment.

Australia

In New South Wales, the proclaimed standard for airborne
dust remains as previously reported at 700 particles per cubic
centimetre in the range 1 to 5 microns.   Most of the coal extracted is won by the bord and pillar system but there exist, never-
theless, a small number of longwall systems and some difficulty is
experienced in these cases in meeting the airborne dust concentration requirements of the Act.   Respiratory protective devices
are used in such cases.   Plastic-type material is now being
largely used in place of jute for brattice and exhaust fans with
steel ducting becoming increasingly favoured for face ventilation
when using continuous miners.   With relation to roof support,
roof bolting is becoming more generalised.   A new method of
extracting pillars known as the "shortwall" method was introduced,
making use of modified self-advancing hydraulic supports in conjunction with a continuous miner and shuttles cars.   Results have
been encouraging both in terms of production and of improved roof
control.   Shot-firing for coal winning has been practically
eliminated, methods not requiring the firing of shots now rep-
resenting 94 per cent of the total production.   The trend towards
mechanisation continued to increase during this period as is shown
in table 57.

Table 57

Australia (NSW) – Daily average production (raw coal)

As at June	Open cut	Long-wall and short-wall	Bord and pillar								All mines
			First working			Pillar extraction			Total	
			Loaded by			Loaded by				
			Hand	Machine	Total	Hand	Machine	Total		
	tons	tons	tons	tons	%	tons	tons	%	tons	tons
1954	5 775		13 505	36 162	81.1	11 587		18.9	61 254	67 029
1960	2 882		3 196	46 838	70.2	1 941	19 314	29.8	71 289	74 171
1964	2 688		1 340	50 766	60.4	892	33 365	39.6	86 363	89 051
1968	9 125	248	253	73 747	59.5	225	50 163	40.5	124 388	133 761
1969	12 687	6 326	158	78 097	55.9	70	61 584	44.1	139 909	158 922
1970	18 016	7 371	110	86 328	57.8	60	63 198	42.2	149 696	175 083
1971	16 311	4 543	38	83 451	56.3	117	64 812	43.7	148 418	169 272
1972	26 330	5 632		82 011	53.5	118	71 058	46.5	153 187	185 149

Australia (Contd)

Table 58

Australia (NSW) - Underground haulage - daily tonnage
of raw coal hauled as at June, 1972

	South Mait-land	North West	New castle	West	Burra-gorang Valley	South Coast	Total
Machine loaded to shuttle cars, then coal transported by -							
Conveyor belts	8 803	10 413	50 992	9 095	21 506	30 361	131 170
Conveyors and locos	1 158	..	6 902	..	2 589	11 058	21 707
Locomotives	..	..	..	454	..	..	454
Rope	..	196	..	71	..	..	267
Shuttle car to surface	..	133	..	..	..	..	133
Total via shuttle cars (a)	9 961	10 742	57 894	9 620	24 095	41 419	153 731
Machine loaded (other than to shuttle car) then coal transported by -							
Conveyors, face and belt	..	..	..	..	..	4 266	4 266
Conveyors, rope (and horse) ...	472	66	..	..	..	..	538
Rope (and horse)	166	..	..	..	..	..	166
Total	638	66	..	..	..	4 266	4 970
Hand loaded and coal transported by -							
Rope and horse	..	118	..	..	..	..	118
Total hand loaded	..	118	..	..	..	..	118
Total daily tonnage	10 599	10 926	57 894	9 620	24 095	45 685	158 819

(a) includes 1,799 tons via front-end loader-transporters.

Australia (Contd)

The use of scraper loaders has been practically discontinued and now represent only 0.3 per cent of the total production of coal in New South Wales. Rules relating to the ventilation of NSW coal mines are set out in the Seventh Schedule of the Coal Mines Regulation Act (No. 37 of 1912) as amended and provide, inter alia, for minimum air quantities in the working places and, where combined cutting and loading machines or continuous miners are operating, for a quantity of not less than 5,000 cubic feet of air per minute passing the person operating such machines.

In Queensland, dust counts are made by the Inspectors of Mines during their regular inspection visits. The larger mines also employ their own dust samplers. Water is used liberally and as many of the mines are naturally wet, instances of excessive dustiness are rare. During the period under review there has been a substantial increase in the use of mobile diesel trackless equipment and their use has necessitated the provision of increased ventilation and of methods of dust suppression. Methods used include the provision of additional ventilation, the use of water sprays at sources of dust production, the use of dust extraction systems at underground dumping points and crushers. Underground roadways have in many cases been surfaced with concrete and in other cases the salt crust process is used extensively. Steel supports and rock bolts are used in addition to timber to maintain good roof conditions. The use of sprayed concrete has also been introduced for roof control. Research has been conducted into the pattern of mining, the size and shape of excavations in the metal mines with a view to improving ground control. In the weaker strata of the coal mines, methods of mining and sequence of extraction are carefully chosen to minimise the effect of excessive ground pressures. With regard to stowing and packing, the cut-and-fill stopes of the Mt Isa Mines make use of de-slimed tailings, while in the sub-level open stopes a mixture of crushed smelter slag, de-slimed tailings and cement is used for this pur- pose. The filling is conveyed by water and hence dust free. All drilling underground is wet. Blasting in the metalliferous mines is performed using one or more of the following methods: safety fuse; electric delay detonators; anodit delays; or by using cordtex detonating fuse with detonating explosives for this detonators. It is of interest to note that the increasing use of raise borers has reduced the amount of blasting to be performed while the increasing mechanisation of coal cutting and loading operations has virtually eliminated the use of explosives for this purpose. Coal-getting machines, which include drum-shearers mounted on armoured conveyors and continuous mining machines, are all fitted with dust suppression sprays. The use of pneumatic picks has practically been discontinued. At the larger coal and metalliferous mines, all loading, transport and unloading of ores, coal and waste rock is done with the assistance of machinery. Suitable ventilation arrangements, including auxiliary ventilation, are provided to ensure that the dust produced is directed into the return ventilation circuit. Some hand loading and tramming is used in the smaller operations and in such cases the ore, etc. is kept damp. Where belt conveyors are in operation, use is made of sprays and, in some cases, of exhaust ventilation. Roadways are kept clear of deposited dust by the liberal use of water which enables such dust to be carried away as sludge. Dust produced in crushing stations, treatment plants and other permanent installa- tions is handled through extraction systems using filtration or precipitation devices such as wet cyclone scrubbers, automatic bag filters and electrostatic precipitators.

Australia (Contd)

In South Australia, wet drilling is used throughout all underground operations and the use of water sprays for dust suppression is generally practiced. Water-feed drills are also used in some quarries where other methods of dust suppression include the surfacing of roads and the imposition of speed limits. Dust on roadways is also allayed by the use of water cars and, in some instances, by laying clean gravel.

In the mines of Tasmania, the standard applied for dust of less than 5 microns is as follows:

120 p.p.c.c. - good;
150 p.p.c.c. - acceptable under certain conditions;
200 p.p.c.c. - bad.

Dry drilling with dust extraction from the collar of the hole is practiced in open-cut metalliferous mines while in the coal mines, cutters and loaders are fitted with water sprays. In the case of transport by scrapers and conveyors, the ore is kept wet. Sprays are commonly used to allay dust in crusher and treatment plants, with local dust extraction in certain cases.

Large-scale mining is relatively new in the Northern Territory. Underground mines are mainly in the Tennant Creek area which has a hot, dry, inland sub-tropical climate. Dust suppression is done with water supplied through hoses and sprays, wet drilling is performed, and exhaust ventilation is installed. Water from surface catchments is piped underground. Mining methods include open-cut, long-hole open stoping, sub-level stoping and square set timber stoping. Increased dust created by mechanical loading is combated by providing large surface fans with adequate return airways. In regard to surface drilling, it is of interest to note that in some quarries good results have been obtained through using detergent tanks with wagon drills to prevent excessive dust production. A reduction has been achieved in the amount of secondary blasting, particularly on grizzleys, by making use of hydraulic rock splitters. Surface crushers have sprays fitted at all dust-producing points and the largest crushing section at Tennant Creek has been provided with a 12,500 cfm dust extractor and filter connected to the secondary and tertiary crushers, screens and selected transfer points. Severe dust conditions are encountered in the quartzite and iron ore quarries and although water sprays are used, operators need to wear dust respirators at certain workplaces. Most loading is done by mechanical loaders, scrapers or through chutes in shrinkage stopes. Extensive use is made of conveyors for transport to and from the mill and crushing plants and these are notable sources of dust production. Transport by trucks or mine cars gives rise to dust at loading and tipping places which has been limited by the use of water sprays. The use of sprays underground has given rise to difficulties from corrosion and from clogging.

In Victoria, dust control is exercised by wetting and by dilution through adequate ventilation. In surface mines, roadways are surface treated or regularly wetted to allay dust. Most coal faces and floors are naturally damp, and dust does not present a big problem. Stringent precautions are taken in treatment plants including wet crushing, enclosure and dust extraction. Where modern equipment such as tunnel boring machines and trackless mining equipment, attention to dust has been necessary but the conventional methods of control are still practiced. It is noted that all new crushing or treatment plants to be constructed in a metropolitan area are required by law to instal total enclosure and dust extraction equipment where necessary.

Austria

As reported previously, the Austrian Office for Combating Dust (OSBS) continues to exercise responsibility for sampling and investigating airborne dust, as well as for the development of protective measures.   While most mines are supplied with piped water, difficulties of supply to a number of small mines in Alpine regions have been overcome by making use of water tanks connected to the compressed-air system so as to provide the necessary water pressure for dust suppression purposes.   Extensive use is made of sprays or atomisers for dust allaying in all phases of the mining operations, including mechanised coal-getting, and in all the phases of loading, transport and unloading of mineral and rock where in some instances self-actuating sprays have been installed. With regard to ventilation a minimum requirement has been set of $2 \ m^3/min$ per person;   in the case of mines where the risk of fire-damp or dust explosion exists, this figure is raised to $3 \ m^3/min$; and, where diesel-powered equipment is in operation, an amount of at least $6 \ m^3/min$ per HP is required.   Provision has also been made for the installation of auxiliary ventilation in all working places where through ventilation does not exist.   The Austrian standard for the respirators for use in mines (ÖNORM F 5304), referred to in the previous report, has been supplemented by a further standard for their testing (ÖNORM F 5305).   Attention is drawn to the problem of working places where the temperature reaches 30° C or more, and where the use of water for dust suppression purposes can lead to high relative humidity and insupportable working conditions.

Belgium

In spite of the development of techniques for dust prevention and suppression, the use of water remains the principal method. Pneumatic drills with axial water feed are used for the development of drives.   Haulages are watered down regularly and hygroscopic salt used for consolidating deposited dust.   Table 59 shows the growth of dust prevention practices during the period under consideration.

Table 59

Dust prevention methods related to
percentage production - Belgium

Method used	Percentage of production				
	1968	1969	1970	1971	1972
Atomisers	14.8	10.3	19.2	34.8	44.1
Water infusion	61.1	61.4	60.2	50.1	43.7
Deep infusion of seam	-	3.9	6.7	5.1	2.7
Other methods	19.0	18.5	7.5	3.8	1.8
No method in use (including seams naturally wet)	5.1	5.9	6.4	6.2	7.7

Belgium (Contd)

Most of the coal is won by making use of caving methods as is shown in table 60.

Table 60

Roof support method related to
percentage production - Belgium

Method	Percentage of production				
	1968	1969	1970	1971	1972
Stowing	17.9	13.6	15.2	13.4	11.4
Caving	82.1	86.4	84.8	86.6	88.6

Blasting is largely used for the advancement of tunnels and shafts and represents 86 per cent of all such work performed in 1972. The remaining 14 per cent was in soft rock using pneumatic picks.

The use of pneumatic picks has largely diminished and has been replaced by mechanised methods as is shown in table 61.

Table 61

Methods of breaking coal - Belgium

Method	Percentage of production				
	1968	1969	1970	1971	1972
Pneumatic picks	31.7	24.1	21.3	14.4	12.2
Mechanised	68.3	75.9	78.7	85.6	87.8

Dust produced during loading and transport and unloading is allayed by watering down or with the aid of atomisers.

Burma

Water is used extensively for dust suppression and all drilling is wet. Some mechanisation of mineral handling has been introduced, making use of small scrapers. Main haulage is by mechanical means. Watering down of broken rock after blasting is practised Rail transport of workers to and from the working place is provided in certain instances. Supervisors are expected to ensure that dust prevention and suppression measures are applied. In the lead, zinc and silver mines high temperatures and humidities present a special problem.

Canada

In <u>Alberta</u>, the Division of Industrial Health Services
monitors all operations to ensure compliance with the standards
imposed and acts in an advisory or consultative role in the
implementation of preventive techniques.

In <u>British Columbia</u> water with detergent is used for dust
suppression purposes in surface drilling operations.   In winter,
a mixture of water and alcohol or warm water is used to combat
low temperatures.   In some cases, dry drilling with exhaust is
practised.   Most underground mines are ventilated by mechanical
means, but some smaller mines rely on natural ventilation with
auxiliary mechanical ventilation.   All mines using diesel powered
equipment underground are required to instal mechanical ventilation.
Ventilating air requirements are based upon the air flow required
by permit to operate diesel powered equipment or an amount of
50 cu.ft. per minute of air per square foot of face area, which-
ever is the larger.   In general an air velocity of 50 ft. per
minute is maintained in all but the very large open stopes.   All
working places must be supplied with water, all drilling must be
done with water and water is sprayed wherever blasting takes place.
In narrow-ore bodies various methods of open stoping are practised
and all stopes must have two entrances to facilitate ventilation
and dust control.   Where longhole drilling is practiced, the
larger blasts are done at the weekend to allow a longer clearance
period for the gases and dust.   Rock bolting is widely practised.
Back-filling is done with non-dust producing material such as
glacial till or mill sands, but in one case sink-float rejects are
used which give rise to high-dust concentrations and the area concerned is isolated to prevent the exposure of workers.   Certain
open-pit mines use large rotatory or diesel-electric powered
drills which are equipped with water feed and/or "Rotoclone"-type
dust collectors.   Power shovels and front-end loaders are used to
load rock.   There has been a recent trend towards the use of
diesel-powered LHD (load-haul-dump) units in underground mines.
Dust control is effected by the use of water and by the supply of
adequate ventilation.   All crushing plants and assay sample preparation areas are required to be equipped with exhaust-type dust
control systems.   In the case of the asbestos mills, dust control
is effected by using exhaust systems with bag-type filter units.
Supervision of dust control and prevention is generally done by
the safety department of the mine in conjunction with the operating
staff.   Under the heading of special problems it is noted that
freezing temperatures create difficulties in the use of water in
crushing plants and to this is added the problem of static elec-
tricity in conjunction with the conveyors used to transport minerals.

In <u>Manitoba</u> water is supplied to all working places and used
to allay dust.   Adequate ventilation for dilution and the use of
exhaust systems is ensured under the supervision of a ventilation
engineer to maintain satisfactory levels of dust concentrations.
Wet drilling is compulsory in all underground locations and blasting operations are confined to the end of the shift.   Conventional
track and trackless equipment is used for loading and transport of
mineral and rock, diesel operated equipment is used extensively and
ventilation requirements are generally based on the criteria developed for diesel operation.   Atomisers or sprays are used after
blasting and at loading and transfer points.   Fabric-type dust
collectors are in general use and in some cases wet-type centrifugal

Canada (cont.)

collectors have been installed.   Diesel-operated man carriers
are used for the transport of personnel over long distances.
Reference is made to the need for a suitable instrument and procedure for the gravimetric assessment of dust concentrations in
the vicinity of diesel equipment, as the carbonaceous material
from the diesel exhausts results in the adoption of special procedures which could affect the accuracy of the dust assessment.
The report also refers to the need for further research into dust
suppression and sampling techniques in mining operations such as
rock-breaking equipment and transport systems.   Similarly, reference is made to the need for intensified medical research with a
view to establishing more precise criteria for the development of
suitable instrumentation for dust sampling and greater standardisa-
tion of method.

The report from New Brunswick does not indicate major dust
problems in relation to strip coal operations and in the underground base metal mines the massive sulphide ore does not give
rise to large amounts of airborne dust where water is used for
drilling and for wetting down.   As diesel-powered LHD equipment
is widely used, the high volumes of ventilating air required for
this and other diesel-powered equipment is adequate to maintain
acceptable conditions.   Crushing and screening operations in the
metal mines are enclosed and the dust exhausted to filters or bag
collectors.   A large underground sulphide fire in one mine presented a special problem of gases in the mine but gave rise to no
dust problem.

From a comprehensive report on the coalmining operation in
Nova Scotia, it is noted in particular that modern mechanised
equipment has been introduced both in longwall mining and in mechanised room and pillar systems using double-ended ranging drum
shearers, armoured face conveyors, powered-face supports, belt conveyors, continuous miner loaders and shuttle cars.   Water is
supplied to all the collieries and is applied through sprays on the
mining machines.   Experiments have been made with different types
of shearer drums and different sizes and shapes of cutting picks.
The drums at the time of reporting were fitted for pick-face flushing.   More recent experiments were conducted with hollow shaft
ventilation.   Drilling in advance headings is wet with the exception of one colliery where dry drilling is practised.   Extensive
shotfiring is carried on.   Cleaning up of deposited dust is necessary at all loading points and along conveyors as well as in the
main haulage roads.   No consolidation of deposited dust is done.
Main fans include a 1200 hp forcing fan as well as several exhaust
fans of from 500 to 800 hp.   No particular dust problems are
reported in the surface plant but among the special problems mentioned are the severe winter temperatures which are overcome at
the top of the slopes by using oil heaters, the extreme and very
rapid drops in atmospheric pressure which lead to inflow of methane
gas, and the fact that the rock adjacent to the coal seams has a
quartz content of 40 per cent which results in a measured content of
2-5 per cent in the respirable dust.

New developments in the Province of Ontario include standardisa-
tion on the use of dust collectors on dry drilling equipment in open
pits and quarries.   Some of the deeper mines have installed refrigeration units while in those mines where heating of the mine air
is required, direct-fired natural gas heaters are supplanting the
indirect fired heating units used previously.   A booklet entitled

Canada (cont.)

"Design Guidelines for Dust Control at Mine Shafts and Surface Operations" (second edition, February 1974), published by the Mining Association of Canada has been distributed to all mines and engineering design firms.

It is reported from the Province of Quebec that water in controlled quantities is introduced into the compressed air used for drilling in order to effect control of the dust.   Dry drilling is permitted only in talc mines where the workers make use of dust respirators.   The difficulties attached to operating in the Far North where the ground is permanently frozen are stressed.

In Saskatchewan wet drilling is used throughout all hard-rock mines and water is applied through sprays or atomisers at all dust-producing points.   Dust suppression measures are not so far enforced in the potash mines as present medical evidence indicates that this dust is not injurious to health.   Considerations of comfort have, however, been taken into account in order to reduce high concentrations of airborne dust.   In the open-pit mines some problem has been encountered with dust on roadways and in the preparation plants;   this has been overcome by spraying and by providing better ventilation in the plants.

Cyprus

Dry drilling is not permitted and all handling of ore and rock must be performed in wet conditions in underground mines.   In surface mines dry drilling with dust collectors is permitted. Emphasis is placed on good ventilation in underground mines.   Roadways in the surface mines are maintained in a moist condition by using sprays and in surface treatment plants all processes which cannot be kept wet are provided with exhaust ventilation and dust filtration plant.   Blasting by means of dynamite or ANFO takes place in all mines with the exception of an asbestos open-cast mine where heavy duty bulldozer/rippers are employed.   No special dust problem is reported in these cases.

Czechoslovakia

As previously reported, all machinery or equipment for use underground requires to be certified as being fitted with approved dust suppression devices.   Dust control methods are based, in general, on the use of water and on the provision of abundant ventilation.   These include:

(a) in coal mines - infusion at the coal face;

- the use of sprays or atomisers at the point of attack of coal-getting machinery and in the haulages;

- watering-down of broken coal or rock and the consolidation of deposited dust with the aid of foam;

- drilling with water or foam injection;

Czechoslovakia (cont.)

         - intensive auxiliary ventilation;

         - personal protective equipment is required to be issued to all personnel;

(b) in metal mines - wet drilling or dry drilling with dust extraction;

         - wetting-down of broken rock for loading, transport and unloading;

         - use of water ampoules for tamping and of fog during blasting operations;

         - all blasting at the end of the shift;

         - adequate ventilation of working places after blasting and between shifts;

         - the use of personal protective equipment.

Surface water is supplied for use underground and wetting agents such as "Slovanol 909" and "Alfonal K" have been used in conjunction with face infusion and for drilling or watering-down and have resulted in increased efficiencies of from 1.2 to 10 per cent. Research into the use of foam in connection with these operations commenced in 1971 and have shown encouraging results. Consolidation of roadway dust with magnesium and calcium salts has also been effected.

El Salvador

Water is supplied to the mines from the surface and, in certain cases, fissure water from the mines is recirculated. No particular benefit has been observed from the addition of wetting agents. Beneficial results from the use of water have been obtained and its application is required in all underground operations including drilling, the use of pneumatic picks and transport of mineral.

Finland

The use of water for dust suppression purposes has been extended and improvements made in the ventilation of the mines. Wet drilling is almost universally practised. Exposure to dust from blasting has been reduced by carrying out these operations at the end of the shift and by using smaller explosive charges. Dust respirators are issued for use in particular during drilling and blasting operations.

France

Principal developments during the period under consideration are listed as follows:

- increased use of powered supports;

- cessation of the use of coal cutters in the North/Pas-de-Calais area;

France (cont.)

- mechanisation of steep and semi-steep workings in Lorraine;

- concentration of mining associated with the use of more powerful machinery;

- increased use of shrinkage methods (soutirage) in the wide seams of the Central Midi.

These developments have tended to increase the risk of dust production and so all coal mines are now supplied with water at pressures up to 25 bars, reduced where necessary to 10 bars for infusion.   Very few iron mines have a water reticulation system and in general the water is supplied from containers mounted on the mining machinery.   Most metalliferous mines and those of radioactive and related minerals are provided with water circulation although in some cases drilling machines are fed from tank wagons.   Water for surface operations is supplied to crushers and screening or similar plant.

Dust prevention methods introduced along with these developments include:

- deep infusion from advance headings;

- infusion using long vertical holes from the face;

- the use of atomisers at draw-points in shrinkage workings;

- the use of wire mesh covered with plastic sheets in the roof.

The principal dust hazard in surface quarries is to be found in the crushers and related installations where dust extractors, wet or dry collectors, sprays, etc. have been widely installed.

The use of self-advancing supports has increased in the collieries, as well as the practice of roof bolting in headings, pillar and stall and steep workings.   In such cases, dust prevention is effected by:

- sprays during caving;

- placement of a fabric curtain parallel to the face;

- spraying of the roof before advancing by means of sprays fitted to the heads of the supports;

- in shrinkage systems, the use of mesh and plastic sheets, as mentioned above.

Drilling in coal is generally effected dry but where stone is liable to be intersected, hollow drill steel is used with water introduced through a sleeve attached to the machine.

Shot-firing is becoming less frequent.   Where practised, tamping is employed using ampoules filled with water or other dust-abating liquid solutions.   Water blasts are used during shot-firing in headings and, in Lorraine, the workers make use of refuge places ventilated at a slight over-pressure by means of compressed air. Persons required to enter a dust-filled atmosphere are supplied with compressed air-fed helmets.   The use of pneumatic picks is also

France (cont.)

decreasing: where used the dust is allayed with atomisers.   Coal-
getting machines are fitted with sprays delivering onto the pick
face or cutting surfaces.   Plough faces are provided with atomisers
regularly spaced along the armoured conveyor and controlled by the
operator.

All mineral or rock transported is kept wet, sprays being
installed at loading, transfer or unloading points and in certain
cases dust extraction plant is installed at tips, chutes, etc.   The
development of more effective spray nozzles for producing fog has
continued.   Wet, venturi-type de-dusters have been found effective
when used with exhaust ventilation.   In general, attention has also
been given to the improvement of the ventilation throughout the
mines.

Movement of personnel by foot has largely been replaced by man-
trains, trucks and minibuses and by conveyors or "telesiege-type"
lifts.

Numerous types of dust filtration masks are to be found among
the different mines, but these are becoming less and less accepted
or worn by the men in spite of campaigns designed to encourage their
use.

A dust control department is to be found at the main office of
each colliery, directed by an engineer or a foreman and including
sampling and dust control personnel.   Centralised dust laboratories
are established in each of the main coalfields, and these also carry
out work for the iron and other mines.   The laboratories also take
charge of the training of dust prevention personnel for the mines.
Engineers on the mines are responsible for giving regular instruction to supervisory staff and other persons concerned with dust prevention activities and use is also made of the safety services and
safety meetings to inform personnel on this subject.   In all the
mines, new miners are instructed in dust prevention and suppression
during the apprentice stage and before they commence work underground.

Germany (F.R.)

Underground and open-cast mineworkings are generally equipped
with drinking-water supply systems.   All workplaces with a dust
exposure risk have water supplies.   At 7.5 per cent of the coal
face of the Saar basin where water is infused surfactants are added
to improve the wetting efficiency.

In all coal seams presenting a potential hazard of spontaneous
combustion stowing is done hydraulically.   Pneumatic stowing is
more widely used in metal mining.   Table 62 shows the varying use
of the two stowing methods during the period 1968 to 1972 (in percentages).

Germany (F.R.) (cont.)

Table 62

Pneumatic versus hydraulic stowing
(in percentages)

	1968	1969	1970	1971	1972
Pneumatic stowing	38.0	33.7	29.9	28.7	23.9
Hydraulic stowing	16.8	18.1	20.9	11.3	12.7
Totals	54.8	51.8	50.8	40.0	36.6

Wet drilling has been employed throughout the mining industry. A technique making use of a low-expansion foam (expansion ratio: 6) is still under test.   Shot-firing is performed with the aid of plastic stemming bags filled with water or a special paste.   Tests are under way to replace the water or paste by a calcium chloride powder.   The results are encouraging.

During the period under review winning, loading, haulage and unloading of minerals and muck have become more and more mechanised in both coal and metal mines.   Only 4.6 per cent of the coal faces in North Rhine-Westphalia are not yet mechanised.   The degree of mechanisation at the coal face in the Saar mines is shown in table 63 (in percentages).

Table 63

Year/Mine work	1968	1969	1970	1971	1972
Driving and winning	89.4	91.9	96.1	90.2	97.0

Hand-in-hand with the spread of mechanisation there has been an increase in the variety and scale of means of dust control. Cutter-loaders are equipped with automatic spraying attachments; coal-face water infusion is quite widely used; metal and non-metal mineworkings are equipped with automatic water-spraying systems to wet the roof and walls.   Water is infused over a total length of 75,831 m. of the faces in North Rhine-Westphalia, and of 84 per cent in the Saar mines.   The following dust abatement measures have been taken at all haulage operations:

- automatic spray ramps to wet the minerals at loading and transfer points;

- built-in water spray nozzles at conveyor throw-offs, mine-car tipping points and ore-dumping chutes;

- built-in automatic water-mist curtains in haulage roadways.

Germany (F.R.) (cont.)

In Westphalia 2,852 loading and transfer points are equipped with spraying systems.   Wet methods are generally used to control deposited dust and to abate airborne dust.   Physico-chemical methods are more and more widely made use of for consolidation of dust deposited in haulage roadways.   The total length (in metres) of roadways treated by several of these methods simultaneously is given in tables 64 (Westphalia 1972) and 65 (Saar, 1968-72).

Table 64

Westphalia

Roadways	Physico-chemical methods to control deposited dust			
	Salt pastes	Powders, flakes	Water sprays	Other methods
Rock drivages (m)	83 450	158 055	5 020	21 040
Haulage roadways (m)	245 433	250 454	2 250	-
Totals (m)	328 883	408 599	7 270	21 040

Table 65

Saar

Year	1968	1969	1970	1971	1972
Length of roadways (m)	42 417	42 756	80 988	61 803	53 516

As regards general mine ventilation, the air volume has been increased to improve dust control and working conditions.   Respiratory protection is provided at all sites where technical dust control measures are insufficient.   A stock of 14,500 dust masks are available in the Westphalian mines.

Directives relating to dust prevention and suppression and to routine dust sampling are set out by the Divisional Mining Offices. All working places are linked to the fresh water supply.   Water for dust suppression is supplemented by the use of wetting agents where conditions are considered appropriate.   All phases of operation and working are planned with due regard to dust control, use being made of sprays, sprinklers, wet drilling, water stemming, dry dust extraction and dry and wet filters.   Hydraulic supports are used in more than 90 per cent of the workings and the introduction of shield-type supports has shown favourable results.

Ghana

A ventilation department is maintained at most mines which is responsible for the implementation of dust prevention practices and for regular sampling of the working places. Periodical checks are also carried out by the Dust Control Officer of the Mines Department. Water is supplied at controlled pressure to all working places. Wetting agents are not used. Provisions covering the control of dust produced during drilling, blasting and the transport of ore are set out in Part II of the Mining Regulations, 1970. The use of rock bolts with wire mesh and "shotcrete" has been found effective for the support of pressurised or friable strata. All underground drilling is wet, using jack-hammers with air legs, while dry drilling is used on surface although in one mine churn drills are used with water. Blasting takes place at the end of the shift, being arranged in sequence and followed by a suitable interval so that personnel are not exposed to the dust and fumes. Hand lashing and scrapers or mechanical shovels are used in the extraction of ore after blasting and precautions are taken to ensure thorough wetting down during these operations. Main transfer points are equipped with sprays for dust suppression. The use of water blasts in development ends is general, and auxiliary ventilation is supplied with the aid of electric or compressed air-driven fans. Forcing and exhaust-overlap systems are in use, the discharge of the ducting being kept within 100 feet of the face. All crushing and preparation of ores is carried out in surface plants and the operations are carried out under wet conditions. Dust exhaust systems are being introduced. The use of dust respirators is required for certain personnel in charge of ore transfer and in the crushing plants. New workers are instructed in safety and health matters and production staff receive a briefing on dust control in the ventilation department. With increasing depths of mining, problems are being encountered from excessive temperatures and humidity and the introduction of artificial cooling is at present under consideration.

Honduras

Wet drilling is used in the mines and dry drilling in quarries; water is also used in conjunction with pneumatic picks. Mechanical transport is used for moving mineral and rock with sprays where necessary for the abatement of airborne dust. Periodical inspections are made to check operations for dust prevention.

India

Dust prevention officers are appointed in the coal mines while in the metal mines these duties are carried out by the general supervisory staff. Water is supplied to all underground mines at a pressure of over 5 kg./cm.^{2}. Most coal is worked by the bord and pillar system although some longwall faces are in existence with mechanical cutting, loading and transport in some instances. Hydraulic stowing using sand is practised but does not give rise to a dust problem. As the coal seams are naturally wet, drilling, where used, is by means of electric rotary drills without water and does not give rise to a serious dust problem. Wet drilling is commonly used in the metalliferous mines. Water is used liberally through spraying after blasting and the experimental use of water ampoules for tamping was found to be successful but has not been

India (cont.)

extended due to supply difficulties.   The "Armstrong Airbreaker"
is being used in some mines.   In the coal mines the working face
and the roadway within 60 metres of the face are watered down so
as to ensure that the moisture content of dust does not fall below
30 per cent.   Sprays are used with machine cutters.

Israel

The principal attempts to control dust in mining operations
have been made at the Timna copper mine.   New methods that have
been tried include the use of sprays onto the face to be blasted,
while a second experiment consists of placing nylon water-filled
bags in the blast area.   No information as to results is yet
available.   Water reticulation is provided throughout but the
use of wetting agents has been discontinued since no effective
reduction in airborne dust concentrations could be discerned.
Mining methods have changed to trackless operations employing
jumbo drills, transloaders, shovel dozers and other types of
vehicles.   Transport of ore is by belt and through a vertical
shaft.   All drilling is done wet and mist or fog is used for dust
suppression where necessary.   All transportation of workers underground is by vehicle and haulage ways are sprayed with salt water
from the Dead Sea to consolidate deposited dust.   Discarded engine
oil has also been found to be effective.

Jamaica

The dusts encountered in bauxite mining are inert or of a
nuisance-type only.   In haulages and in quarries water, and in
some instances bunker fuel, is used to allay the dust.   Some use
has also been made of calcium chloride.   The application of water
during the handling of alumina and bauxite is not feasible and
electrostatic or cyclone-type precipitators are used for dust
prevention and suppression.   Drilling is necessary only in limestone or gypsum quarries and in such cases is dry.   Bauxite is
mined by bucket, shovel or dragline, and is transported and handled
mechanically.   A number of "dusty" points exist in the preparation
plants such as transfer and loading points, but these are not considered to present a health hazard due to the non-pneumoconiotic
nature of the dust.   Respirators or masks are supplied for use at
such points.

Malagasy Republic

Mining operations are almost entirely open-cast workings of
which only granite and chromite require dust prevention measures
to be taken.   Among the methods used are:

-   atomisers at tipping points and in crushing and milling
    plants;

-   application of water to the holes during hand drilling;   and

-   wearing of masks during mechanical drilling in quarries and
    during the mechanical handling, transport and unloading of
    mineral and waste rock.

Mexico

Piped water is supplied to all drilling, handling of rock
and mineral, and to crushing and grinding operations.   Wetting
agents are used at particularly dusty points.   Sub-level stoping
is generally practised with pillars left where necessary and use
is made of rockbolts.   Very little stowing or packing is effected.
In the coal mines the longwall caving system is used.   With the
exception of hand drilling where this exists, all drilling of rock
is done with water-feed machines.   In some cases dry drilling is
carried out in coal.   Mineral is broken with the aid of explosives
with continuous miners being used in the coal mines.   Diesel-
driven vehicles are widely used in the metal mines with the mineral
being kept moist.   High expansion foams are used in the coal mines
during transport by conveyor.   Deposited dust in roadways is consolidated by applying water, no special method being practised.
Atomisers are installed where necessary to control airborne dust
particularly at the loading and discharge points of conveyor systems.   Dust extraction and filtration arrangements are provided
at crusher plants particularly where primary crushers are installed
underground.   Primary ventilation of the mines is assured by mechanical means in most cases but natural ventilation is found to be
adequate in certain cases.   Auxiliary ventilation is provided for
development headings.   Airline respirators and filter masks are
manufactured in Mexico in accordance with various national standards
and their use is required in areas where it has not been found possible to eliminate dust by other means.   In addition to the supervision exercised by the competent authority, safety committees are
formed which maintain a control over dust prevention activities.
Supervisory staff are instructed in occupational hygiene and
workers are instructed in methods of combating dust.   In regard
to the problems of high temperature and humidity, regulations
require temperatures underground to be maintained between 10 and
37 degrees centigrade and the humidity between 20 and 95 per cent.

Morocco

Efforts to introduce mechanised methods of coal-getting have
so far proved unsuccessful because of the narrow width of the seams
being worked and for this reason pneumatic picks are largely used
which give rise to a severe dust problem.   To combat this, the
advancing longwall faces are equipped with sprays throughout,
particular attention being given to loading and onloading points.
Steel arch supports are used in roadways and the faces are sup-
ported by props with waste packs and stowing of waste in the goaf.
Wet drilling is employed in the advancement of roadways and stone
headings.   Coal is removed through chutes, feeding into scrapers
leading to the principal conveyors, dust being allayed with the
aid of sheets of jute sacking kept wet and with atomisers at all
transfer points.   Careful attention is paid to the provision of
good ventilation as an aid to dust prevention.

In the metal mines, the use of water is now general.   Wet
drilling, the use of water ampoules for blasting and sprays where
necessary are the basis of the dust prevention methods in use.
Mining systems in use include pillar and stall, top slicing with
waste packing and shrinkage stoping.   Explosives are used to
break down the mineral, with the aid of pneumatic picks where suitable.   Manual loading is practised in the smaller headings with

Morocco (cont.)

mechanical shovels being used for larger operations.   Mine cars
are used for transport.   Water blasts are used to allay dust after
shot firing.   The wearing of dust masks is required in all workplaces where dust prevention is not entirely effective.

Netherlands

        As in previous years reference is made to the annual reports
of the Dust Institute at Limburg in which a comprehensive account
is given of dust prevention activities in the mines of the
Netherlands.   The closure of coal mines continued to be implemented
during this five-year period and all coalmining will have been discontinued by the year 1972.

New Zealand

        Machine mining was introduced in both the main coal fields,
dust control being effected by the use of water sprays through the
cutter heads of the machines.   Mobile water sprinklers are used
to allay dust on shuttle car roads.   Conveyor belts are fitted
with mist sprays to prevent the spread of airborne dust.   It is
reported that effective control of roadway dust where men travel
has been achieved by applying small quantities of water onto the
floor at intervals.   The moisture is trodden forward by the men
resulting in a continuing advancement of the compacted surface.
An increasing effort is being made in the training of personnel in
dust prevention and suppression methods.

Norway

        Innovations reported include the introduction of a system of
dust control in quarries and stamp mills known as the "chem-jet"
system.   Developments have also taken place in relation to dust
extraction during drilling.

Pakistan

        The use of drills and pneumatic picks under dry conditions
continues to be widely practised.   Experiments have been made
with wet drilling in stone headings but this created a support
problem due to the abnormal heaving characteristics of the shale
strata.   The use of sprays at loading, transfer and unloading
points has been introduced in a number of coal mines.   Deposited
dust in coal-mine roadways is usually removed manually.   Recently-
introduced legislation enables the competent authority to prescribe the use of respiratory protection for persons employed in
mines.

Panama

        Wetting-down of the rock is practised in the quarries and
masks are used where required.   No underground mines are worked.

Philippines

Dust prevention and suppression practices are an integral part of all normal mining operations. Water is supplied systematically to the working places, no wetting agents are used. All drilling underground is wet. Where dry drilling is used on surface, dust extractors are employed or the personnel are supplied with respirators. Dust extraction systems are provided for crusher houses and conveyor lines.

Poland

Dust prevention and suppression in the salt and potash mines has been achieved with the aid of improved ventilation. In the treatment plants all tipping and transfer points have been enclosed. Use has been made of hydraulic transport in certain instances resulting in improved conditions. Wet drilling is practised and water tamping is used during blasting operations in hard rock. Particular attention is given to the instruction of personnel in dust prevention methods.

Romania

Water reticulation systems are installed in mines both on surface and underground in practically every case. In the lignite mines, where the use of water in conjunction with cutter-loaders has not been practicable due to the nature of the surrounding rock, experiments are being made with dry dust collecting devices. Wet drilling is employed in all types of mines, and for shot firing, where necessary, water ampoules are used for tamping. Dry drilling has been employed in a number of steeply inclined workings and in such cases the period of exposure of personnel in such workplaces has been reduced. With the increase of mechanised working many new systems of dust prevention have been introduced all of which depend upon the use of sprays, atomisers, fog curtains, etc. at loading, unloading and tipping points. On surface, material handled is kept wet and extensive use is made of enclosure with exhaust ventilation. All young workers are instructed in "protection at work" and young miners receive additional training before commencing work.

Singapore

Water sprays are used in all quarries at the primary and secondary crushers, stock-piling points and on conveyors. Trials have been made with a wetting agent in one instance. Drilling is normally dry with shot-firing taking place at break periods when the fewest number of workers are exposed. Four quarries have dust extraction systems in operation using either cyclone or bag filters. In the prevailing high temperatures and humidities, it is found that workers are reluctant to make use of respirators.

Spain

Regular inspection visits are made to the mines by the Inspection Service to control those workplaces which may present a health risk. Most mines have their own water supply but in certain cases

Spain (cont.)

water is supplied from outside sources.   Wetting agents are not
used.   Dry drilling in underground mines is prohibited, only
water-feed machines being permitted, with the exception of machines
fitted with a dust extraction device.   Mineral is broken with the
aid of explosives, a suitable interval being enforced after blasting during which time the ventilation is maintained so as to
eliminate all dust and gases.   The use of water blasts is also
enforced.   In coal mines, injection of the seam is being practised.   Mineral being loaded or transported is kept sufficiently
wet, according to the method in use, to prevent the formation of
dust.   In certain cases exhaust ventilation is used to discharge
the dust into a return air circuit.   Hygroscopic salts are used
to consolidate the dust on roadways where personnel have to travel.
Ventilation quantities are prescribed with a view to maintaining
satisfactory conditions based on the number of persons at work, the
type of work in progress and the natural conditions.   Precautions
taken against dust in preparation plants include the use of exhaust
ventilation, dust filters, precipitators and water atomisers.   A
maximum temperature of 33°C is laid down for underground workings,
above which figure no work may take place.

Sri Lanka

     Piped water is available at all working faces where pneumatic
drilling is done and, while hand drilling is still practised, there
is a trend towards the increased use of mechanical rockdrills which
in all cases are of the water-feed type.   Sorting and preparation
of mineral (graphite) is done on surface in open buildings.   Supervisors are responsible for putting into effect dust suppression
methods and all workers are instructed in their implementation.

Sudan

     The supply of water is a problem, being largely obtained from
wells.   All mineral is wetted for loading and transporting.
Workers are reluctant to use respirators because of the hot climate
in summer when temperatures may reach 117°F.   High winds and sand-
storms add to the difficulties during the winter months.

Sweden

     Few changes are reported concerning the use of water for dust
suppression which is enforced according to instructions issued by
the Industrial Safety Inspectorate.   Wetting agents are not used,
and are not considered to be effective under the conditions encountered.   Reports and directives relating to the protection of
workers against silicosis and to the use of explosives as well as
to research projects related to the present subject were published.
It is reported that a working party was engaged in studying occupational health problems related to grout injection.   Loading machines
and crushing plants have been fitted in certain instances with
sealed cabins having a supply of filtered fresh air.   It is noted
that water sprays are not considered against airborne silicate dust
and in underground applications water scrubbers are widely used for
separating dust from the air.   Industrial hygienists and safety

Sweden (cont.)

engineers are trained by the Industrial Medicine Department of
the National Board of Occupational Safety and Health.   Attention
is drawn to the problem caused in sampling by the presence of oil
mist in the air.

Switzerland

     Piped-water systems are provided to all workplaces with
certain exceptions in the high mountain regions where water has
to be transported.   Wetting agents are not used.   In addition
to the traditional methods of rockbreaking, the use of tunnelling
machines is becoming more general.   Tunnels are frequently
concrete-lined, but rockbolts with steel mesh and gunite are also
used.   By using the correct mixture with a special machine the
formation of dust during guniting may be avoided.   Wet drilling
is generally practised but during freezing conditions dry drilling
with dust extraction may be used.   Aspiration of dust is also
practised in the quarries.   Loading and transport is entirely
mechanised with the material being kept wet by means of spraying.
Where scrapers are used the rock is watered down.   Dust is
removed from the sidewalls of tunnels by washing and roadways are
suitably treated where trackless vehicles are used.   The use of
wet dust separators (Zyklon type) has been found effective for the
removal of airborne dust.   Atomisers are used in the sorting and
crushing installations.   With regard to preparation plants the
two main problems of stone dressing and sorting and crushing: with
regard to the former dust extraction devices are being perfected.
Satisfactory installations have been provided in the case of sorting and crushing plants.   Dust respirators are not used in tunnelling work.   Supervisors are instructed in the equipment and
operations relating to dust prevention and are responsible for
instructing workers and apprentices in these matters.   The principal special problem is that of low temperatures in the high
mountain regions which create difficulties in regard to water
supply.

Turkey

     During the period under consideration new measures were taken
against dust in the mines.   Water was supplied to many of the
mines and wet drilling introduced so that about 30 to 40 per cent
of the machine drills in use are equipped with water feed.   The
Occupational Safety and Health Centre (ISGUM) provides training
facilities in dust prevention for personnel and has started a
systematic control of the working places with a view to introducing
dust prevention practices.

Uganda

     Mining is by orthodox cut and fill using hydraulic fill.   All
drilling is done wet using axial-feed machine drills.   Working
faces are washed down after blasting and loading is by means of
rocker shovels into side-tipping mine cars.   Water blasts are used
in all development ends.

United Kingdom

The current report deals mainly with the quarrying industry and it is noted that most of the minerals won have an inherent moisture content so that the supply of water to quarries does not present a problem; water is, however, available at most processing plants.   Sprays are used at primary crushers and at mineral transfer points but this may not always be effective in reducing respirable dust levels.   Wetting agents are used in certain instances. The main dust problems arise where mineral has to be dried during processing and this is overcome by using hoods and sealed pressurised hoppers with dust collecting systems.   Dust in haulage and transport is controlled by the use of water sprays and by surfacing, e.g. asphalt, the roads.   Protective equipment used includes dust collectors on hand-held or portable equipment, face masks and respirators including the SMRE dust helmet.   Some research has been done on the use of ventilated control cabins.   Lectures and demonstrations on dust control are given by members of the Inspectorate.

United States

The use of water continues to be the most common practice for the suppression of dust.   In 1969, 79 per cent of the total production of coal came from faces where piped water was available while water was used in addition to ventilation in 98 per cent of continuous miner operations.   Up to 48 sprays may be fitted on these machines using 10 to 25 gallons of water per minute at operating pressures of up to 300 psig using built-in booster pumps. Studies on nozzles were carried out and increased efficiency in dust suppression was achieved with the use of wetting agents. Experimental work was done on the use of foam where laboratory tests showed a reduction of up to 90 per cent in respirable dust. In-mine tests are being conducted.   Experimental work was done on the use of hydraulic pins as a method of roof control with a view to the elimination of mechanical drilling and reducing dust production.   Roof-drilling equipment with integral dust collectors was introduced and satisfactory results were obtained by the introduction of water through the core of auger drills.   The use of water stemming was shown to lead to a reduction in airborne coal dust, particularly when used with a wetting agent.   Reference is made in the report to the increase in the use of continuous mining machines and the decrease in conventional mining systems as well as to the growing trend towards longwall mining, where both shearer and plough-type units are in operation.   Water infusion is little used due to differences both in the mining methods and in the physical characteristics of the coal deposits.   Research into hydraulic mining of coal continued but a practical and economic system for mining has yet to be developed.   It was demonstrated experimentally that dust concentrations at transfer points on belt-haulage ways can be reduced by applying water to the belt surface. The enclosure of transfer points with the use of dust scrubbing devices was also under study.   With regard to the explosion hazard of coal dust, it was shown experimentally that this could be controlled by a proper application of ammonium phosphate, water and dry rock dust and that this method reduced the amount of water required by 11 per cent compared to conventional wetting methods. Other tests were carried out on substances for use in inhibiting coal dust-air flames.   Spray nozzles for controlling airborne dust were further investigated, as was the application of foam and, in the case of surface installations, the use of steam.   The report

United States (cont.)

also describes a number of wet and dry-dust collectors which had
been the subject of extensive study covering their characteristics
and capabilities, the results of which are published. New
emphasis is placed upon the importance of ventilation in the control methods (water, foam, etc.) are only complementary to ventilation as an aid to reducing the total dust load to be removed.
Stress is placed upon adequate face velocities where mining
machines are working and upon the use of auxiliary fans or line-
brattice systems so as to maintain velocities in the region of
100 ft./min.   Reports were published describing a scrubber-testing
programme and also the design and installation of a dust collector
for preparation plants.   A list of approved respirators was published but it noted that the Coal Mine Health and Safety Act
required that the use of respirators shall not be substituted for
environmental control measures.   Details were presented of a
cyrogenic air-supply system designed mainly for continuous miner
operators.   In the field of training, the subject of mine health
received increasing attention and in particular a massive training
programme was started in the sampling and evaluation of respirable
coal-mine dust.

USSR

     A schedule is drawn up for each mine setting out the measures
to be applied for dust prevention purposes.   The list includes
details concerning the water supply, special protective measures
applying to operations where dust is created, ventilation provisions and the supply of material or equipment for dust suppression.
Water of good quality is supplied to all faces and considerable use
was made of wetting agents which were shown by test to have varying
degrees of effectiveness.   Foam as an agent for the inhibition of
dust was used with good effect particularly in thin steeply dipping
seams where it was found possible to surround the area in which
drilling was taking place with a blanket of foam, thereby reducing
the airborne dust concentration.   Atomisers and sprays are used
at loading and transfer points.   Where shotfiring is practised,
the area is liberally watered down before blasting and recourse is
had to water ampoules for stemming and to the use of water curtains.
The use of compressed air/water blasts in preparatory workings is
practised.   The use of water alone has not proved sufficient in
the case of mining machines such as cutter-loaders which are
equipped with a standardised form of dust exhaust.   Stress is laid
on the importance of ventilation as a primary aid to dust prevention, optimum air velocities being recommended from 0.5 m/sec. to
2.0 m/sec. at the working face.   Where airborne dust concentrations
exceed the maximum permissible the use of respirators is required of
which there are two types in common use.

Venezuela

     Methods of dust suppression employed during the construction
of five tunnels are described in the report.   Systems of ventilation used include forced or reversible fans with steel or plastic
ducting.   Broken ground is watered down during loading operations
and drilling is carried out using jumbo rigs with water-feed drills.
In some cases use is made of pneumatic picks.   Diesel trackless
vehicles provide the transport of rock, the roadways being watered
down to consolidate dust.

Zambia

Regular dust sampling is carried out on all copper mines, during which operations the water-feed tubes of the rock-drills in use are checked.   No dry drilling is practised.   Water is supplied to all working faces and no wetting agents are used. Sprays are used on conveyor belts and ore being transported is kept wet.   A number of underground dust filters are in use and these are maintained daily in good condition by personnel using dust respirators.   In some cases where dust has given rise to a problem on roadways, these have been successfully treated by using old sump oil.   Refrigeration has been employed in certain areas where rock temperatures over 117°F have been recorded. Acclimatisation of the workers is practised and encouraging results have been obtained with the experimental use of ice jackets.

PART III

AIRBORNE DUST SAMPLING, MEASUREMENT AND ANALYSIS

———————

Australia

Dust sampling procedures remain largely as described in previous reports.   It is noted, however, that in New South Wales work is in hand to consider the suitability of the MRE Gravimetric Sampler for bord and pillar workings, while in Queesland the Watson konimeter has been largely replaced by the thermal preci-pitator and tests were made with the modified thermal precipi-tator using a diffraction size analyser.   The thermal precipitator and the Draeger Dust Sampler were examined in Victoria as an alternative to the Watson konimeter.   The modified thermal precipitator is also used in South Australia.

Austria

Dust sampling continues to be performed with the aid of the HS konimeter but it is noted that an automatic counting system has been introduced.

Belgium

Dust sampling is carried out with the aid of the Soxhlet Thimble.   Sampling at the rate of about 1 m^3 per hour is effected during the active working period over a minimum period of two hours.   The instrument is placed at head height in the return from each working place and about 15 to 20 metres from the face with a minimum distance of 25 cm. from the roof.   Where piped ventilation is used, the sampling position is 10 m. from the end of the ventilation volumn with the forcing system, and at the entry to the column with the exhausting system.   The filter is dried before and after sampling at about $85^{\circ}C$ until a constant weight is obtained and the quantity of dust expressed in milli-grammes is obtained by taking the difference in weight of the filter before and after sampling, the result being expressed in mg./m.^{3}.   The content in incombustible dust is obtained by intro-ducing the sample in a porcelain crucible into an oven at $600^{\circ}C$, heating it up to $700^{\circ}C$ over a period of half-an-hour, and main-taining it at this temperature for a further half-hour.   After slow cooling, the residue is weighed and the operation repeated to ensure complete combustion.   Working places are classified and reweighed taking into account the dust content and the percentage of incombustibles, being grouped into classes I, II and III.

Canada

Dust sampling is carried out by the mining companies and by the competent authorities in the different provinces.   Table 66 shows the different instruments that have been reported as being in use during the period under consideration.

Table 66

Dust sampling instruments in use - Canada

Province	Types of instrument
Alberta	MRE Sampler, Hexhlet, High-Volume Samplers, Personal Samplers, Nylone Cyclone, BCIRA Cyclone.
B. Columbia	Konimeter, Gravimetric with midget impinger for coal and asbestos.
Manitoba	Konimeter (gathercole type) for routine, Gravimetric.
Nova Scotia	MRE Sampler.
Ontario	Gravimetric (long-running type).
Quebec	Midget Impinger.
Saskatchewan	Konimeter (gravimetric sampling to be introduced).

The report from Ontario Province makes special mention of the problem of asbestos dust and states that "the latest reduction in TLV from 5 fibres/ml. greater than 5 microns in length to a standard of 2 fibres/ml. greater than 5 microns in length can be achieved in the asbestos mines and process plants of the Province and in fact in many cases this standard has been achieved". It also makes reference to the problem of the radiation hazard resulting from the inhalation of radionuclides. A directive for Ontarion mines presenting this hazard is included in the report. Inter alia, this directive prohibits smoking underground in uranium mines and provides for exposure limits to radon daughters and for their monitoring and recording of results, as well as for the use of respirators where these limits cannot be maintained. The requirements apply to all mines where radon daughter concentrations exceed 0.3 WL.

Cyprus

Procedures have been described in previous reports. It is of interest that airborne dust concentrations are specified in the Regulations as follows:

Cyprus (cont.)

Substance	Allowable concentration (p.p.c.c.)
Asbestos	180
Chrome	700
Dust (nuisance no-free silica)	1 800
Portland cement	1 800
Silica: high (above 50 per cent free SiO_2)	180
medium (5 to 50 per cent " ")	720
low (below 5 per cent " ")	1 800

All particles in the range 0.5 to 5 microns are counted and, in the case of asbestos, all fibres are counted.

Czechoslovakia

A standard system of sampling was introduced in 1970. It is based on the use of fibre filters together with a two-stage system of aspiration which ensures the separation of the respirable dust fraction, and is followed by a gravimetric assessment of the dust collected.   A granulometric analysis is made of the dust collected and the silica content is determined.   Regular sampling is performed at fixed intervals according to the nature of the working place.

German Democratic Republic

Routine samples were taken as laid down by GDR standard TGL 22311 (1968) - Occupational hygiene - Maximum allowable workplace concentrations.   A type 10 VEB Carl Zeiss/Jena konimeter is used for sampling.   Samples are analysed by light-field photomicrography.   The fibre (asbestos) and quartz content of the samples is determined by X-ray diffractometry.

Finland

Dust samples are collected on filters and measurements made of the content of dust by weight.

France

The system of dust sampling and classification of workplaces has been described in previous reports.   In the North/Pas-de-Calais region, special rules have been applied since 1968 by which four classes of workplaces are distinguished, according to which the "dust factor" is less than 0.5; between 0.5 and 1.25; between 1.25 and 2.50; and greater than 2.50.   Miners are allocated to working places on the advice of the medical officer who makes a determination on the basis of five categories of worker according to their fitness and of the classification of the workplace according to the dust factor.

Gabon

External irradiation in the uranium mines is controlled by means of individual dosimeters and the results recorded on cards. Weekly samples are collected from each workplace and the average dose per working hour is calculated.

Dust samples are taken monthly for each working place and for each type of work.

Germany (F.R.)

The sampling and measurement remain as described in previous reports. In 1971 a new list of MAC values for dust containing quartz and for quartz dust was published.

In Westphalia a special plan has been established for continuous dust sampling by means of the tyndalloscope. A filtering system (type BAT-I) has been used to determine the quartz content of the respirable fraction. Another system frequently used for analysing dust samples is the Dräger SFJ sampler MPG-I. In the BAT-I filter system the coarse particles are retained in a cyclone, while the fine particles collect on a membrane filter. The Dräger sampler makes use of the air stream to fractionate the particles. It contains a set of plates for retaining the coarse particles and a series of membrane filters arranged after the plates for analysis of the fine particles.

The Saar mines use a routine sampling system comprising the tyndalloscope and konimeter. In 1972 the elaboration of new standards for collieries was started on the lines of the recommendations made by the Commission for the Improvement and Hygiene of Working and Environmental Conditions in Mines. These standards apply to the threshold limit of SiO_2 in respirable dust fractions, measuring equipment, dust control techniques, etc. The Commission presently analyses the results obtained so far in view of the general application of the standards.

Ghana

As previously reported, the konimeter continues to be the instrument in general use. In some cases, the thermal precipitator has been introduced. Routine sampling is carried out monthly.

India

Routine dust sampling is performed in the Kolar Gold Mines using the thermal precipitator. The Directorate-General of Mine Safety has recently acquired two gravimetric dust samplers with a view to fixing threshold values in the coal and metalliferous mines, while use is also made of the midget impinger, by means of which samples are collected on an ad hoc basis.

Israel

Gravimetric and konimeter methods of sampling are employed, using the Casella sampler, the Hexhlet and the cascade impactor. Counting of dust samples containing asbestos is done on millipore filter paper.

Mexico

Dust sampling is carried out from time to time making use of the midget impinger.

Morocco

Dust sampling is effected in each working place every second month. Samples are collected using the Turbo-collector as used in France, whose procedure for calculating a "Pneumoconiotic index" is also followed.

Peru

The midget impinger is used for dust sampling, samples being taken at the working place at intervals of between 5 and 30 minutes. Working places are visited monthly. Standard methods of counting are used with a Whipple-type eye-piece graticule. Membrane filters using Whatman millipore filters are employed. Both gravimetric evaluation and chemical evaluation for free silica of the samples are performed. Results are recorded and the records maintained by the Safety and Health Division of the Ministry of Energy and Mines and by the Occupational Health Institute of the Ministry of Health.

Romania

Routine dust sampling is carried out at least quarterly at all workplaces where airborne dust concentrations have been found to be above the maximum permissible levels, and at least once a year at all workplaces where these levels have not been exceeded. Samples are generally taken with the impinger and, in a few cases, with the aid of filters.

Singapore

After the introduction of the Sand and Granite Quarries Act, 1971, quarry owners have been required to have periodical dust sampling carried out making use of personal samplers. Results are checked by the Industrial Health Unit. The midget impinger continues to be used for other sampling purposes.

Spain

New legislation being introduced is designed to bring about the replacement of snap sampling by continuous sampling and to eliminate the counting of dust under microscope. Directives relating to sampling positions require that samples be taken on the return side of a working place at a distance not exceeding 15 m. from the last working operation. Where auxiliary ventilation is in operation, samples are taken between the face and the ventilation pipe entry in the case of exhaust ventilation, and 10 m. behind the delivery end of the column in the case of forcing ventilation. Where ventilation is obtained by diffusion, the sample should be taken not less than 15 m. from the face and at a distance from the principal entry of one-and-a-half times its cross-section. Sampling points are also laid down for mineral transfer points,

Spain (cont.)

crushing and grinding plants, and other dust-producing points.
All particles less than 5 microns are taken into consideration
and silica content is analysed by X-ray diffraction. A pneumoconiotic dust index is established using the formula:
i = 3.32 log Ct - k as described in previous reports.

Sri Lanka

     Instruments used for sampling in underground graphite mines,
open granite quarries and graphite curing sites are the Owen's Jet
Counter and the midget impinger. Sampling is performed upon
request from management or from the employees' organisations.
Particle counting and size determination are done under oil-
immersion and petrographic and gravimetric analyses are made to
estimate the free silica content of the dust. Values obtained
are correlated against the published TLV figures of the American
Conference of Governmental Industrial Hygienists. Records are
maintained and a statistical analysis of the data to correlate
dust concentrations with the fractional lung volumes of the exposed working population is intended to be embarked upon.

Switzerland

     A recent inquiry carried out by the Swiss National Accident
Insurance Association (SUVA) has recommenced the adoption of an
apparatus for sampling, known as the SUVA 70, based on the use of
a probe whereby the dust particles are collected on a filter.
Details of the apparatus and its use as well as the procedures
for determining the dust concentration, particle size and quartz
content have been included in separate reports. A main feature
of the new apparatus is the ability to provide rapid information
on the airborne dust concentrations at the working place.

Turkey

     Dust sampling is undertaken by the Occupational Safety and
Health Centre (ISGUM) at Ankara using a gravimetric method.

United Kingdom

     New sampling procedures were introduced during the period of
the present report. These have been described in a booklet
entitled "Approved Conditions for Airborne Dust - Standards and
Procedures for Sampling", reference F4040. Briefly, standards
have been set for (i) stone drivages - 3.0 mg/m^3 and, (ii) for all
other locations - 8.0 mg/m^3. Samples are taken throughout the
working shift at set frequencies. The coal faces, which are sampled monthly, are classified on the basis of the mean of the
monthly concentrations of the last three months. Other places
are classified initially on the basis of the first sample taken,
and where any sample exceeds the standard, the place must be re-
sampled the following month and is then re-classified on the basis
of that result. The instrument used is the NCB/MRE Type 113A
gravimetric dust sampler. An instrument used for weighing gravimetric samples is accurate to 0.00001 g. For determining the

United Kingdom (cont.)

quartz content of a sample an infra-red spectro-photometer is
used.   All results are recorded and transmitted to the respective
headquarters and collieries and access to a computer is available
for the preparation of annual reports.

United Arab Republic

Use is made of the midget impinger and the konimeter for airborne dust sampling together with a microscope and a microscope
for counting and measurement.   Analyses for free silica have been
made of dusts from the iron ore mines and the phosphate mines.

United States

A detailed and extensive report provides information on publications and recent developments in the field of sampling, measurement and analysis of respirable airborne dust.   From the report it
emerges that the midget impinger continues to be used as an
engineering control instrument, but its use has been supplanted in
the evaluation of health hazards of dusts, mainly by the two-stage
respirable mass samplers.   The standard for coal-mine dust was
based on dust concentrations measured with the MRE instrument, but
the Act provides for the use of alternate approved sampling devices
and concentrations measured with such instruments are subsequently
converted to equivalent MRE concentrations.   A personal respirable
dust sampler was designed, constructed and tested by the Bureau of
Mines.   It is noted that in the case of devices using the 10 mm.
nylon cyclone, conflicting flow-rates have been reported and only
the 1.7 and 2.0 l pm. have been legally accepted as flow-rates for
use in enforcing health standards.

Investigations are reported covering the effect of pulsating
flow on dust collected by personal samplers and also on the per-
formance of respirable dust samplers with fibrous dust.   The
sampling requirements of the Federal Coal Mine Health and Safety
Act of 1969 are also cited in the report.

An interesting concept that has been developed by the Bureau
of Mines is that of "high-risk" with reference to dust exposure
in bituminous coal mines.   This concept states that if the dust
concentration of the worker exposed to the highest respirable dust
concentration is below the mandatory standard, then it is assumed
that all other workers in that section will be below that concentration.   For example, the cutting machine operator in a continuous
mining section is so designated, and sampling is based upon this man.

In the case of metal and non-metallic mines, the relevant Act
enforces the TLV values adopted by the ACGIH.   For mineral dusts
with a content greater than 1 per cent quartz, respirable gravimetric sampling is carried out, while for mineral dusts containing
less than 1 per cent quartz, a total dust gravimetric sample is
collected.   Asbestos is sampled using open-face, 37 mm. diameter
cellulose membrane filters and analysed by phase contrast microscopy.

In relation to dust counting, an account is given of the use
of a Coulter counter to determine the collection efficiency of the
midget impinger for coal dust samples using isopropanol, ethanol

United States (cont.)

and water as the collecting fluids.   A study of the effect of
humidity on light-scattering methods is also described, as also
was a size analysis comparison between sieving and the Coulter
counter.   Several newly developed dust mass monitors are reported
as well as instruments using light-scattering principles.   A new
type of filter for dust sampling has a smooth polycarbonate surface
and cylindrical pores and these have the advantage of having less,
more uniform weight, increased resistance, transparency and of
being non-hygroscopic.

A survey was published covering the methods of analysis of
respirable dust and a method for determining airborne trona dust
concentrations is described.

The results of all respirable coal mine dust sampling are pro-
cessed through a computer which can, with a very short delay,
transmit all pertinent information required for the purpose of
determining compliance with the Act.   Records concerning medical,
examinations and autopsy information are maintained by the examin-
ing authority or other body.

USSR

Standards in mg/m^3 laid down for maximum permissible dust
concentrations are based on maximum values in the working area and
not the average during a shift.   They are designed to prevent not
only pneumoconiosis but also the dust-related bronchial conditions.
Samples are taken in the different workplaces in the breathing
zone of the worker.   Apparatus used includes the AERA and AER-4
portable aspirators and, for operational checking, the DPV-1 dust
sampling appliance.   Records are kept at the mines up to a period
of ten years.

Zambia

Sampling instruments in use include the konimeter for routine
monitoring of airborne dust in the working places.   The slides are
treated to remove salts and combustible materials and are counted
with the aid of a microscope.   The maximum concentration allowed
is taken as 350 particles per cm^3.   The Hexhlet sampler is used
for sampling respirable airborne dust over a period of up to eight
hours, sampling at a rate of 100 l/min. for particles less than
10 microns in diameter;   these samples are analysed by chemical
and X-ray diffraction methods for mineral content and for free
silica.   Use is also made of the long-running thermal precipitator
for evaluation of particles by electron and optical microscopy and
of the MRE-type 113A and the personal sampler TI3050.   Mine water
is examined for dust particle content with the aid of the nephelo-
meter.   It is intended to transfer part of the recording programme
onto computer.